Framework 7

MATHS E

HOMEWORK BOOK

David Capewell   Westfield School, Sheffield

Marguerite Comyns   Queen Mary's High School, Walsall

Gillian Flinton   All Saints Catholic High School, Sheffield

Geoff Fowler   Maths Strategy Manager, Birmingham

Kam Grewal-Joy   Mathematics Consultant

Derek Huby   Mathematics Consultant

Peter Johnson   Wellfield High School, Leyland, Lancashire

Penny Jones   Mathematics Consultant, Birmingham

Jayne Kranat   Langley Park School for Girls, Bromley

Ian Molyneux   St. Bedes RC High School, Ormskirk

Peter Mullarkey   School Improvement Officer, Manchester

Nina Patel   Ifield Community College, West Sussex

OXFORD
UNIVERSITY PRESS

OXFORD
UNIVERSITY PRESS

Great Clarendon Street, Oxford OX2 6DP

Oxford University Press is a department of the University of Oxford.
It furthers the University's objective of excellence in research,
scholarship, and education by publishing worldwide in

Oxford   New York

Auckland   Cape Town   Dar es Salaam   Hong Kong   Karachi
Kuala Lumpur   Madrid   Melbourne   Mexico City   Nairobi
New Delhi   Shanghai   Taipei   Toronto

With offices in

Argentina   Austria   Brazil   Chile   Czech Republic   France   Greece
Guatemala   Hungary   Italy   Japan   South Korea   Poland   Portugal
Singapore   Switzerland   Thailand   Turkey   Ukraine   Vietnam

Oxford is a registered trade mark of Oxford University Press
in the UK and in certain other countries

British Library Cataloguing in Publication Data

Data available

ISBN 0 19 914883 X
ISBN 978 0 19 914883 7

10 9 8 7 6 5 4

The photograph on the cover is reproduced courtesy of
Pictor International (UK)

The publishers would like to thank QCA for their kind permission to use
Key Stage 3 SAT questions.

Typeset by Tech-Set Ltd, Gateshead, Tyne and Wear

Printed in Great Britain by Bell and Bain, Glasgow

About this book

Framework Maths Year 7E has been written specifically for students who have gained a Level 5 or above at the end of KS2. The content is based on the Year 8 teaching objectives from the Framework for Teaching Mathematics.

The authors are experienced teachers and maths consultants, who have been incorporating the Framework approaches into their teaching for many years and so are well qualified to help you successfully meet the Framework objectives.

The books are made up of units based on the medium-term plans that complement the Framework document, thus maintaining the required pitch, pace and progression.

This Homework Book is written to consolidate and extend the Core objectives in Year 7, and is designed to support the use of the Framework Maths 7E Student's Book.

The material is ideal for homework, further work in class and extra practice. It comprises:
◆ A homework for every lesson, with a focus on problem-solving activities.
◆ Worked examples as appropriate, so the book is self-contained.
◆ Past paper SAT questions at the end of each unit, at Level 5 and Level 6 so that you can check students' progress against National Standards.

Problem solving is integrated throughout the material as suggested in the Framework.

Contents

1 Write three sequences with fourth term 8 and fifth term 10.

2 Write three sequences that start 1, 2, …

3 Write down the first five terms of these sequences:

    a The first term is 1, each term is three times the previous term.

    b The first term is 80, each term is half the previous term.

    c Each term is five times the term number.

    d Each term is the cube of the term number.

4 The "Fibonacci Sequence" is:

$$1, 1, 2, 3, 5, 8, 13, …$$

    a How does this sequence work?

    b If you can, find out where the Fibonacci Sequence exists in nature.

    c The "Tribonacci" sequence begins 1, 1, 1, … How might it continue?

5 This is Pascal's Triangle:

```
            1
          1   1
        1   2   1
      1   3   3   1
    1   4   6   4   1
  1   5   10   10   5   1
```

    a What could the next row of the triangle be?

    b Describe any patterns you can find in the diagonals of this triangle.

A1.2HW | Sequences and rules

1 Use the numbers in the box to write five terms of the following sequences:

13		6	16		8
	19	1		9	
		17	11		7
5			10	14	

a First term is 5 with a term-to-term rule of add 3.

b First term is 17 with a term-to-term rule of subtract 4.

c This sequence has a position-to-term rule of add 4.

d This sequence has a position-to-term rule of multiply by 3 and add 4.

2 Copy and complete the following table:

Sequence	Term-to-term rule	Position-to-term rule
3, 7, 11, 15, 19, …	Start at 3 and add 4	Multiply by 4 and subtract 1
5, 9, 13, 17, 21, …		
7, 16, 25, 34, 43, …		
20, 39, 58, 77, 96, …		
$\frac{1}{2}$, 1, $1\frac{1}{2}$, 2, $2\frac{1}{2}$, …		

3 Are these statements true or false? Explain your answers:

a A sequence, beginning with 4 and going up in threes, will reach the number 97.

b A sequence which has a position-to-term rule of 'multiply the position by itself' will reach the number 170.

c A sequence which comes down in twos will eventually reach the number ⁻20.

4 Write a term-to-term rule and a position-to-term rule for:

a The odd numbers.

b The square numbers.

1 For each sequence shown:

a Draw the next two patterns.

b Write down how many counters would be in the 10th pattern.

c Work out how many counters are needed in the 100th pattern.

(**Hint:** If you find it difficult, a table like this one might help you get started.)

Pattern no.	1	2	3	4
No. of counters				

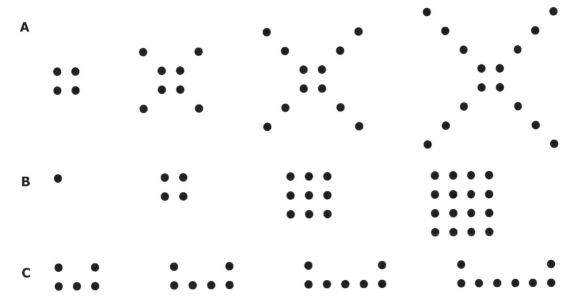

2 A square jigsaw is made up of corner pieces (C), edge pieces (E) and middle pieces (M).

C	E	E	E	E	C
E	M	M	M	M	E
E	M	M	M	M	E
E	M	M	M	M	E
E	M	M	M	M	E
C	E	E	E	E	C

How do I know that a 100 by 100 jigsaw will have 4 corner pieces, 392 edge pieces and 9604 middle pieces? Explain why.

How do I know I have counted all the pieces?

1   The position-to-term rule of a sequence can be shown using a function machine.

position ⟶ | rule | ⟶ term

Draw function machines for these sequences.

(**Hint:** Some may have more than one operation.)

a   4, 8, 12, 16, 20, …

b   11, 12, 13, 14, 15 …

c   6, 11, 16, 21, 26, …

d $\frac{1}{4}$, $\frac{1}{2}$, $\frac{3}{4}$, 1, $1\frac{1}{4}$, …

2   Here are two function machines:

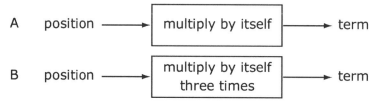

A   position ⟶ | multiply by itself | ⟶ term

B   position ⟶ | multiply by itself three times | ⟶ term

a   For the function machine in A, write down and learn the first fifteen outputs. What special name can we give these outputs?

b   Write down and learn the first six outputs of B. What are these outputs called?

c   This function machine generates a special sequence called triangular numbers. What are the first ten?

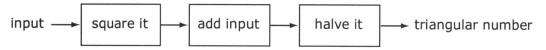

input ⟶ | square it | ⟶ | add input | ⟶ | halve it | ⟶ triangular number

3   In this machine, I must divide by two to get back to my input.

input ⟶ | × 2 | ⟶ output

What must I do in these cases?

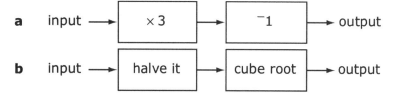

a   input ⟶ | × 3 | ⟶ | ⁻1 | ⟶ output

b   input ⟶ | halve it | ⟶ | cube root | ⟶ output

1 Here are four function machines:

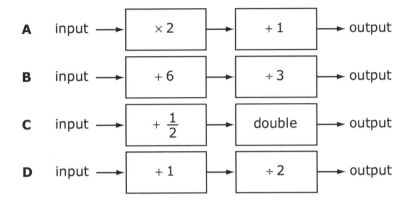

A input → × 2 → + 1 → output

B input → + 6 → ÷ 3 → output

C input → $+ \frac{1}{2}$ → double → output

D input → + 1 → ÷ 2 → output

a What is the output of machine C when the input is 20?

b Which machine gives the biggest output for an input of 11?

c Which two machines always give the same output? Explain why.

d Find an input which gives the same output when put through machine B or D.

2 At a fairground, you pay £1 to play a game.

You roll a dice and put the number into one of three function machines.

If your output is even, you win £2, if not you lose. Which machine is the best to go on?

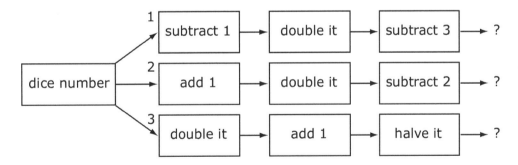

1 subtract 1 → double it → subtract 3 → ?

dice number

2 add 1 → double it → subtract 2 → ?

3 double it → add 1 → halve it → ?

3 Find the missing functions in this machine:

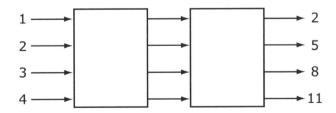

1 → → → 2
2 → → → 5
3 → → → 8
4 → → → 11

1 Algebra worms perform functions like function machines.
They work from head to tail.
Copy and complete the Algebra worms, filling in the missing
spaces with expressions written using algebra.
Worm A is completed for you.

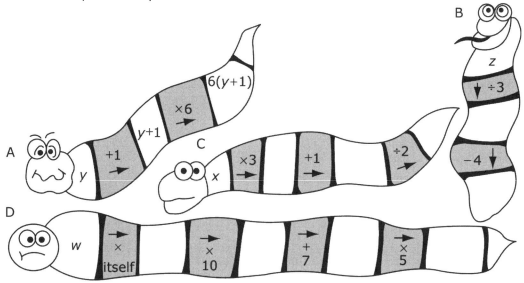

2 Draw your own worm whose tail end has these expressions in:

a $6x - 1$

b $\dfrac{x + 4}{5}$

c $x^3 - 2$

d $3(2x^2 + 7)$

e $10 \left(\dfrac{5x + 1}{4} - 3 \right)$

3 A worm turns an input of 5 into an output of 25.

Give the expression in the tail end if the worm did:

a 1 operation.

b 3 operations.

4 Draw your own worm which:

a Makes all positive inputs bigger.

b Makes negative inputs positive.

c Makes even numbers odd.

Level 5

Jeff makes a sequence of patterns
with black and grey triangular tiles.

The rule for finding the number of tiles
in pattern number N in Jeff's sequence is:

number of tiles = 1 + 3N

pattern
number
1

pattern
number
2

pattern
number
3

a The **1** in this rule represents the **black tile**.

What does the **3N** represent? *1 mark*

b Jeff makes **pattern number 12** in his sequence.

How many **black** tiles and how many **grey** tiles
does he use? *1 mark*

c Jeff uses **61 tiles** altogether to make a pattern in
his sequence.

What is the number of the pattern he makes? *1 mark*

d Barbara makes a sequence
of patterns with **hexagonal** tiles.

Each pattern in Barbara's sequence
has **1 black** tile in the middle.

Each new pattern has **6 more grey**
tiles than the pattern before.

Write the rule for finding the number
of tiles in pattern number N in
Barbara's sequence. *1 mark*

pattern
number
1

pattern
number
2

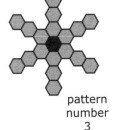

pattern
number
3

e Gwenno uses some tiles to make a **different** sequence of
patterns.

The rule for finding the number of tiles in pattern number N in
Gwenno's sequence is:

number of tiles = 1 + 4N

Draw what you think the first 3 patterns in Gwenno's sequence
could be. *2 marks*

| A1 | **Sequences and functions** |

This is a series of patterns with grey and black tiles.

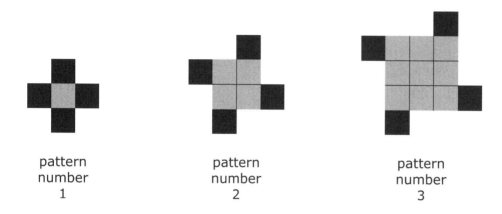

| pattern number 1 | pattern number 2 | pattern number 3 |

a   How many grey tiles and black tiles will there be in pattern number 8?   *1 mark*

b   How many grey tiles and black tiles will there be in pattern number 16?   *1 mark*

c   How many grey tiles and black tiles will there be in pattern number P?   *1 mark*

d   T = total number of grey tiles and black tiles in a pattern.
      P = pattern number.

      Use symbols to write down an equation connecting T and P.   *1 mark*

1 Different civilisations in history have used different number systems.

The Romans used a system of letters for numbers of different values.

```
I = 1
V = 5
X = 10
L = 50
C = 100
D = 500
M = 1000
```

They also used place value in a different way.

A letter of lower value before a bigger one meant subtraction.
For example: IV = V-I = 5-1 = 4

A letter of lower value after a bigger one meant addition.
For example: VI = V+I = 5+1 = 6

a Put these Roman numbers in order, smallest first:
I IX II V VI III VIII X IV VII

b Write the year of your birth in Roman numbers.
For example, 1990 would be MDCCCCXC.

c Put these numbers on a number line (1 to 100):
V L LV LXXI XX C XL

2 a Find out about number systems from other civilisations.
For example, you might research:
◆ Ancient Egyptian numbers
◆ Mayan numbers
◆ Gujurati numbers.
You may find some information in an encyclopedia in the library
or you could search the internet.

b Write a short report on your findings, using no more than 100 words.
The report may include:
◆ A description of the number systems
◆ When they were used and by whom
◆ What made them easy to use
◆ What made them difficult to use.

Look at the number grid.

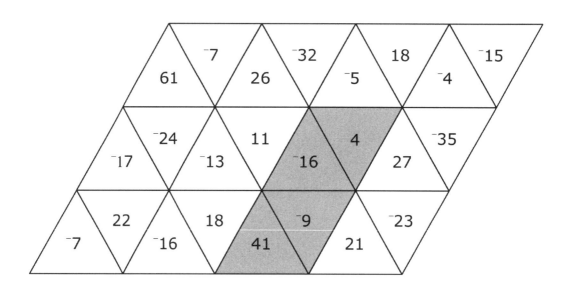

The shaded shape is a four-number parallelogram.

The numbers in the parallelogram add up to 41 + ⁻9 + ⁻16 + 4 = 20

1   Which four-number parallelogram has the highest total?

2   Which four-number parallelogram has the lowest total?

1 Complete these multiplications and divisions:

a $^-3 \times$ ___ $= {}^-21$ **b** $^-10 \div$ ___ $= {}^-5$

c ___ $\times {}^-5 = 30$ **d** $8 \div$ ___ $= {}^-4$

e $^-4 \times$ ___ $\times {}^-2 = {}^-48$ **f** ___ $\div {}^-4 = {}^-6$

g ___ $\times$ ___ $\times$ ___ $= {}^-36$ **h** $^-12 \div$ ___ $= {}^-2$

2 Complete this multiplication grid:

×		3		$^-4$
			15	12
				$^-20$
2		6		
	12			24

3 Work out these sums:

a $^-3 \times (2 + 5)$

b $^-4 \times ({}^-5 + 8)$

c $12 \div (2 - 8)$

d $14 \div ({}^-10 + 3)$

e $({}^-2 \times 3) + ({}^-6 \times {}^-4)$

f $({}^-5 \times {}^-2) - ({}^-4 \times 3)$

g $({}^-20 \div 5) + (8 \div {}^-2)$

h $({}^-24 \div {}^-6) - ({}^-18 \div {}^-3)$

For you to do . . .

Design a poster to explain how to:

◆ Add decimals mentally such as 15.2 + 6.3

◆ Subtract decimals mentally such as 12.8 – 4.9

Your poster should describe the different methods you can use.

Your methods should include:

◆ partitioning

◆ compensation

Here is a reminder:

Partitioning	253 + 325
Write the larger number first for addition	325 + 253
Break the smaller number into place value parts	325 + 200 + 50 + 3
Add/subtract the 100s Add/subtract the tens Add/subtract the units	525 + 50 + 3 575 + 3 578
So:	253 + 325 = 578

Compensation	276 + 398
Round the number and write the compensation	276 + 400 – 2
Use the rounding	676 – 2
Then compensate	674
So:	276 + 398 = 674

This square has a number written at each of its corners:

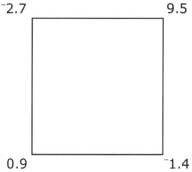

1   Calculate the difference between each pair of corner numbers and write it in the middle of the appropriate side.

2   Join these middle numbers to make a new square inside the first square.

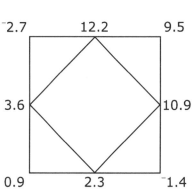

3   Now repeat the process for the new square.

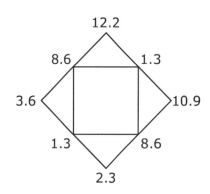

4   Repeat the process until you reach zero.

◆   **Investigate** how many steps it takes for different starting numbers.

◆   Can you **predict** how many steps it will take just by looking at the starting numbers?

◆   How many steps would it take if you used numbers with two decimal places?

1   Estimate the number that the arrow is pointing to:

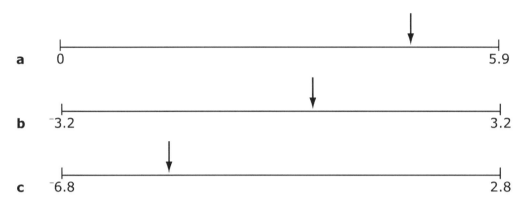

a   0 .... 5.9

b   ⁻3.2 .... 3.2

c   ⁻6.8 .... 2.8

2   Miriam records how long it takes for her to get to work one particular week. These are her times:

47 minutes, an hour and 11 minutes, 52 minutes, an hour and three minutes, 38 minutes.

a   Use a mental or written method to find the total length of time Miriam took in getting to work that week.

b   Key 'an hour and 11 minutes' into your calculator. What does the display read?

3   Identify and explain the error made by somebody using a calculator in these calculations.

a   £25.12 + 32p = £57.12

b   £9.89 – £1.79 = £8 and 1p

c   ⁻£13.25 – £9.58 = ⁻£3.67

4   Calculate the following using a mental or written method, or where appropriate using your calculator.

Carry out a mental approximation to check the answer given on your calculator.

a   7.621 + 3.49

b   15.74 – (2.801 + 3.973 + 8.21 + 6.195)

c   23.884 – ⁻5.291

d $\dfrac{9.29 - 5.08}{9.29 + 5.08}$

Level 5

Here is a list of numbers:

⁻7   ⁻5   ⁻3   ⁻1   0   2   4   6

You can choose some of the numbers from the list and add them to find their **total**.

For example:

6   +   ⁻1   =   5

a   Choose **two** of the numbers from the list which have a **total** of **3**.   *1 mark*

b   **i**   Choose **two** of the numbers from the list which have a **total** of ⁻**1**.   *1 mark*

   ii   Choose **two other** numbers from the list which have a **total** of ⁻**1**.   *1 mark*

c   What is the **total** of **all eight** of the numbers on the list?   *1 mark*

d   Choose the **three** numbers from the list which have the **lowest possible total**.

   Write the three numbers and their total.

   You must not use the same number more than once.   *2 marks*

Level 6

Look at these number cards.

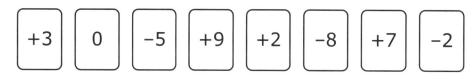

a   Choose a card to give the answer 4.

$$+2 + -5 + \boxed{} = 4$$

1 mark

b   Choose a card to give the **lowest** possible answer.
Copy and fill in the cards below and work out the answer.

$$-2 + \boxed{} = \text{---------}$$

2 marks

c   Choose a card to give the **lowest** possible answer.
Copy and fill in the cards below and work out the answer.

$$-2 - \boxed{} = \text{---------}$$

2 marks

d   Now choose a card to give the **highest** possible answer.
Copy and fill in the cards below and work out the answer.

$$-2 - \boxed{} = \text{---------}$$

2 marks

Remember:

◆ The area of a rectangle is length × width.

◆ The perimeter of a rectangle is 2 × (length + width)

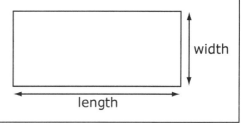

width

length

1 The perimeter of a square is 36 cm. Find the area of the square.

2 Give the area and perimeter of this shaded shape.

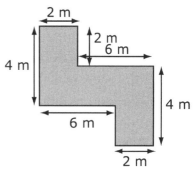

3 A farmer has a roll of fencing 40 m long.
What is the largest area of grass he can contain within a rectangular plot?
Copy and complete this table to help you.
You should calculate the area for at least five more rectangles.

12 m

Example: 8 m   12 m + 12 m + 8 m + 8 m + = 40 m

Dimensions of field	Area of field
12 m by 8 m	96m²
	Maximum area =

4 There is a pond in a corner of the field.
Estimate its area, using the dimensions given.
Explain any method that you have used.

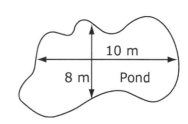

10 m

8 m   Pond

Remember:

◆ Area of a triangle
= $\frac{1}{2}$ (base × perpendicular height)

◆ Area of a parallelogram
= base × perpendicular height

◆ Area of a regular trapezium = $\frac{1}{2}$ (sum of parallel sides) × height

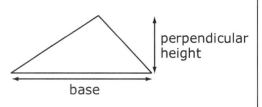

1 A parallelogram has base 23.9 m and a perpendicular height of 41.3 m. Estimate the area of the parallelogram.

2 Find the area of these triangles.

a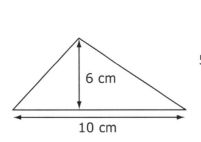

b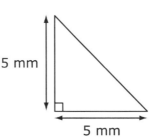

c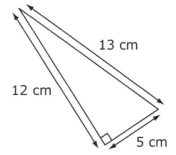

3 A right-angled triangle has area 20 cm². Two of its sides are equal in length. What are the lengths of the equal sides?

4 Find the area of these parallelograms and quadrilaterals.

a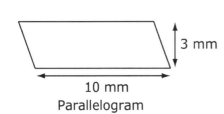
Parallelogram

b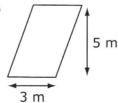
Parallelogram

c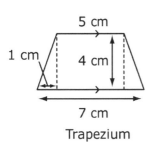
Trapezium

d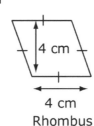
Rhombus

e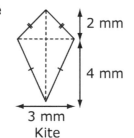
Kite

a   Make a scale drawing of a room in your house.

Include all large items of furniture.

b   Draw up a table giving estimates and the actual measurements of each item in your drawing in real life and say what scale you have used.

c   State the floor area taken up by each item of furniture and estimate the amount of free floor space left in the room.

Is the room full or empty? Give a reason.

Here is an example:

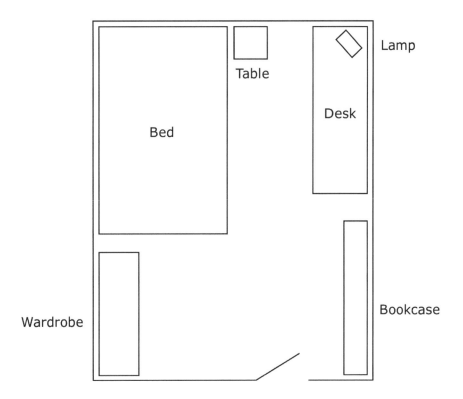

Remember:

◆ Area of a triangle = $\frac{1}{2}$(base × perpendicular height)

◆ The area of the net of a 3-D shape is called the **surface area**.

◆ The **volume** of a 3-D shape is the amount of space it contains.

◆ The volume of a cuboid = length × width × height

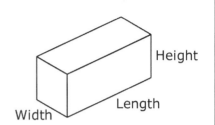

For each shape in questions **1** to **5**:

◆ Write down the number of faces, vertices and edges it has.

◆ Draw an accurate net.

◆ Find its surface area.

◆ Find its volume.

1 Cube of side 4 cm.

2 Cuboid 3 inches by 5 inches by 2 inches.

3 Cuboid 2.5 cm by 6.3 cm by 1.1 cm.

4 Triangular prism: length 5 cm and ends equilateral triangles with sides 4 cm.

You will have to measure the appropriate lengths on your net to find the area of the triangles.

5 Tetrahedron with all edges 4 cm.

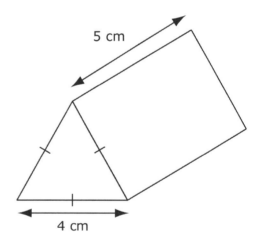

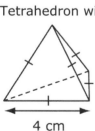

Note: A tetrahedron is a four-sided solid shape where each face is a triangle. To find the area, you will need to measure the perpendicular height of the triangles (as in question 4).

Perimeter and area

a The diagram shows a rectangle **18 cm** long and **14 cm** wide.

It has been split into **four smaller rectangles**.

Copy the diagram below and write the **area** of each **small rectangle** on the diagram.

One has been done for you.

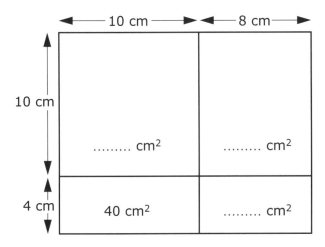

i What is the area of the **whole** rectangle? *1 mark*

ii What is **18 × 14**? *1 mark*

b The diagram shows a rectangle (**n + 3**) cm long and (**n + 2**) cm wide.

It has been split into **four smaller rectangles**.

Copy the diagram below and write a **number** or an **expression** for the **area** of **each small rectangle** on the diagram.

One has been done for you.

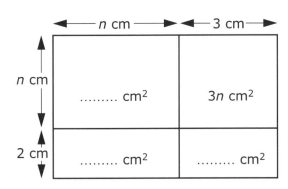

1 mark

Each shape in this question has an **area** of **10 cm²**.

a Calculate the height of the parallelogram.

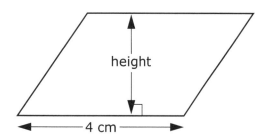

1 mark

b Calculate the length of the base of the triangle.

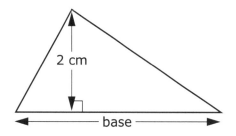

1 mark

c **i** What might be the values of *h, a* and *b* in this trapezium?

(*a* is greater than *b*)

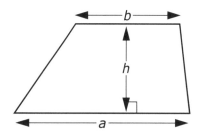

1 mark

ii What else might the values of *h, a* and *b* be? *1 mark*

Egyptian fractions

The ancient Egyptians only used unit fractions, that is fractions with a numerator of 1. An exception to this was their use of $\frac{2}{3}$.

1   Draw a rectangle measuring 3 cm by 4 cm.

2   Divide it into three parts that are $\frac{1}{2}$, $\frac{1}{3}$ and $\frac{1}{6}$ of the whole shape. Make sure none of the parts overlap.

3   Can you find another way to divide the rectangle into parts so that each part is a unit fraction?

4   Draw a rectangle measuring 4 cm × 5 cm. Try dividing it into parts so that each part is a unit fraction. Colour each part using different colours.

5   Investigate what other sizes of rectangles can be divided and completely coloured in using different fractions with a numerator of 1.

1 Copy and complete these number patterns by finding the values of the letters:

    a $\frac{1}{4}$, $\frac{5}{16}$, $\frac{3}{8}$, a, b

    b $\frac{2}{3}$, a, $\frac{5}{6}$, b, 1

    c $\frac{3}{8}$, a, b, c, $\frac{1}{2}$

2 Invent two number patterns involving fractions of your own.

3 Find the fraction which is exactly halfway between:

$$\frac{6}{7} \text{ and } \frac{2}{3}$$

4 Find in its simplest form:

    a $3\frac{9}{10} - \frac{2}{5}$

    b $\frac{12}{13} + \frac{5}{13}$

    c $2\frac{1}{6} + \frac{7}{9}$

    d $\frac{3}{12} - \frac{1}{24}$

5 Rearrange these fractions in order, starting with the largest.

$$3\frac{5}{6}, 2\frac{1}{7}, \frac{23}{3}, \frac{16}{9}, 3\frac{8}{9}, \frac{16}{7}.$$

Mixed ferry crossings 2

A ferry boat has three lanes for vehicles.

Lane 1
Lane 2
Lane 3

The lanes are each 10 m long. The vehicles must all be loaded onto the ferry with none left behind.

Invent a problem

1   Invent and solve a ferry crossing problem of your own. Use 10 vehicles with different lengths expressed as fractions, and try to ensure that their total length is very close to the total length of the lanes.

2   In practice, there should be at least $\frac{1}{4}$ m gap between vehicles.
How could this change your answer to question 1?

3   If the smallest vehicle allowed on is $1\frac{1}{3}$m, what is the ferry's maximum capacity?

Investigation

In a room there are three tables, each with 10 chairs around them.

On Table 1 there is one chocolate bar.

On Table 2 there are two chocolate bars.

On Table 3 there are three chocolate bars.

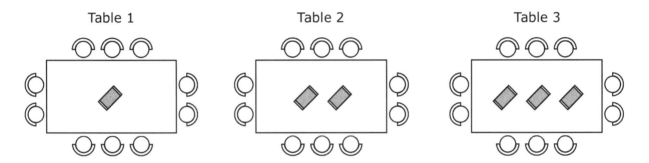

There are 10 people waiting to enter the room one at a time.

Each person must choose to sit at one of the tables.

After all 10 people have entered, the chocolate on each table is shared between the people sat around it.

1   Investigate where each person should sit to get the most chocolate as they enter the room.

For example:

Person 1 sits at Table 3 because it has the most chocolate.

If Person 2 sat at :

◆   Table 1 – 1 bar

◆   Table 2 – 2 bars

◆   Table 3 – $\frac{3}{2}$ bars.

So they sit at Table 2.....

2   Investigate what happens if six more people enter the room one at a time.

Challenge

1 $\frac{7}{5} \times 35$ $= 7 \times \frac{1}{5} \times 35$

                  $= 7 \times 7$

                  $= 49$

Make up five more multiplications with fractions with the answer of 49.

2 $\frac{4}{7} \times 11$ $= 4 \times \frac{1}{7} \times 11$

                  $= 44 \times \frac{1}{7}$

                  $= 6\frac{2}{7}$

Make up five more multiplications with fractions with the answer of $6\frac{2}{7}$.

3   Calculate:

     a $\frac{1}{6}$ of 136 cm.

     b $\frac{3}{11}$ of 26 kg.

     c $\frac{2}{5}$ of £45.

     d $\frac{13}{15} \times 52$

     e $\frac{1}{7} \div 15$

     f $\frac{3}{8} \div \frac{8}{9}$

     g $\frac{2}{9} \times \frac{1}{3} \times \frac{1}{5}$

Loop cards

Design a set of loop cards to practise learning the equivalence of fractions, decimals and percentages. Here is an example of a loop card.

Answer	Question
$\frac{1}{5}$	45%

A complete loop of four would look like this:

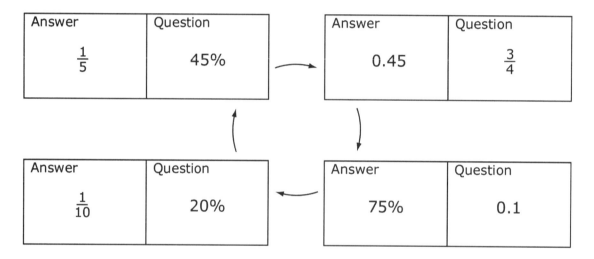

You should try to create a loop of 10.

Use mixed numbers and improper fractions if you wish.

Level 5

The table shows some percentages of amounts of money.

	£10	£30	£45
5%	50p	£1.50	£2.25
10%	£1	£3	£4.50

You can use the table to help you work out the missing numbers.

a   15% of £30 = £_____   *1 mark*

b   £6.75 = 15% of £_____   *1 mark*

c   £3.50 = _____% of £10   *1 mark*

d   25p = 5% of £_____   *1 mark*

Level 6

a   In a magazine there are three adverts on the same page.

Advert 1 uses $\frac{1}{4}$ of the page.

Advert 2 uses $\frac{1}{8}$ of the page.

Advert 3 uses $\frac{1}{16}$ of the page.

In total, what **fraction** of the page do the three adverts use?
Show your working.   *2 marks*

b   Cost of advert: **£10** for each $\frac{1}{32}$ of a page.

An advert uses $\frac{3}{16}$ of a page. How much does the advert cost?

1 mark

1 For each set of data:

    i Work out the median, mode and range.

    ii Which measure gives the best indication of an average value and why?

    iii Decide what the information could represent and who might use it.

    a 3°C, 2°C, 4°C, 3°C, 1°C, –1°C, 3°C, –2°C, 2°C

    b 11 mm, 13 mm, 10 mm, 9 mm, 11 mm, 12 mm, 15 mm, 15 mm, 10 mm, 11 mm, 10 mm, 8 mm, 13 mm, 15 mm, 10 mm, 11 mm

    c 3.1, 2.4, 2.5, 3.4, 2.7, 3.2, 2.5, 3.1, 2.6, 3.5, 2.5, 3.1, 3.2, 2.5, 3.0, 2.5, 3.1, 2.3, 3.3, 2.5, 3.1

2 For each set of data:

    i Work out the median and mode.

    ii Decide which measure is most typical of each set of data.
        Give a reason for your answer.

    a Shoe sizes of a pop group: 5, 7, 8, 6, 4, 7, 5

    b Heights of children at a playgroup:
        98 cm, 105 cm, 120 cm, 95 cm, 107 cm, 125 cm, 119 cm, 125 cm, 100 cm

    c Cost of a litre of petrol: 79.9p, 81.9p, 78.9p, 81.9p, 83.9p, 79.9p, 82.9p

    d Length of TV programmes one evening:
        30 mins, 50 mins, 30 mins, 1 hour, 40 mins,
        1 hour, 20 mins, 1 hour 35 mins, 5 mins, 2 hours

3 The tally charts shows the price of different chocolate bars in a sweet shop, in March and April. Work out the median and the mode of the price for each month.

Price of a chocolate bar	March	April
28p	||	|||
30p	|||	||||
32p	||	
35p	|||	||
36p				

1 Find the mean of these sets of data:

a Number of sweets in a packet:

9, 12, 7, 13, 11, 8, 11, 14

b Height of plants in a greenhouse:

20 cm, 24 cm, 21 cm, 25 cm, 22 cm, 19 cm, 23 cm, 22 cm, 24 cm, 21 cm

c Time taken to run 100 metres:

10.2 s, 9.8 s, 10.0 s , 10.4 s, 9.7 s, 10.5 s, 10.3 s, 9.9 s, 10.4 s, 10.3 s

d Weight of cartons on a plane:

45 kg, 52 kg, 48 kg, 45 kg, 53 kg, 52 kg, 48 kg, 50 kg, 47 kg, 55 kg

2 Find the mean of these sets of data:

a

Shoe size	Frequency
4	3
5	4
6	5
7	2

b

Weight (kg)	Frequency
42	1
43	2
44	5
45	5
46	4
47	3

3 Use your knowledge of the mean to answer these questions:

a A runner averages 10.2 s during 4 races over 100 m.

He ran 9.9 s, 10.7 s and 10.0 s in the first three races.

What was his time in the fourth race?

b The mean number of pins in a box is 25.

Four boxes are opened and three of them contain 22, 26 and 24 pins.

How many pins would you expect the fourth box to contain?

c A photo lab processes 12 films per hour on average during a 7 hour day.

If they process 13, 10, 11, 15 and 12 in the first 5 hours, how many would you

expect them to process in the last 2 hours?

d The average of 3 numbers is 9. What could the numbers be?

This population pyramid shows the population of men and women,
by age group, in the United Kingdom in 1998.

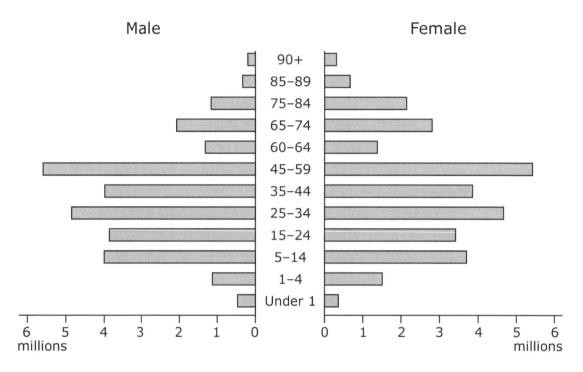

1   Describe the main features of the population pyramid,
    emphasising the differences (if any) between males
    and females.

2   a   Roughly how many men were aged between 15 and 24?

    b   Roughly how many women were aged between 35 and 59?

3   Use the graph to estimate the total population of the UK in 1998.
    Give your answer to the nearest million.

4   a   Roughly what percentage of the total population are males
        aged 65 or over?

    b   Roughly what percentage of the total population are
        females aged 65 or over?

5   Describe in your own words why the government might need
    to know the statistics shown in this graph.

Bags of beads

Class 7C are playing a game of chance with a bag of beads.

There are two teams: the boys and the girls.

Their teacher has three bags of black and white beads.

Bag 1	Bag 2	Bag 3
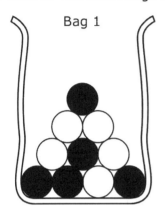	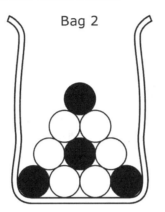	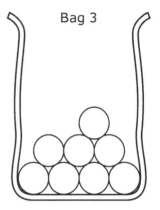

◆ She pulls a bead out of one of her bags.
  ◆ If it is white the boys get a point.
  ◆ If it is black the girls get a point.
◆ She then puts the bead back and pulls out another one.
◆ The first team to get 20 points wins the game.

1 Which team is most likely to win the game if the teacher uses:

    a   bag 1   **b**   bag 2   **c**   bag 3?

Give your reasons in each case.

2 Mark the probabilities of these events on a number line from 0 to 1. Use fractions.

    A: The girls win using bag 1   D: The boys win using bag 1

    B: The girls win using bag 2   E: The boys win using bag 2

    C: The girls win using bag 3   F: The boys win using bag 3

```
├─────────────────────────────────────────────────┤
0                                                   1
```

3 Choose how many black and white beads should be placed in a bag so that it is:

    a   very unlikely but not impossible for the boys to win.

    b   impossible for the girls to lose

    c   slightly biased towards the boys

    d   totally unbiased to either side.

The youth club

At the youth club they have a 'lucky chance' game in operation.

They have a bag containing the letters F, A, T and E.

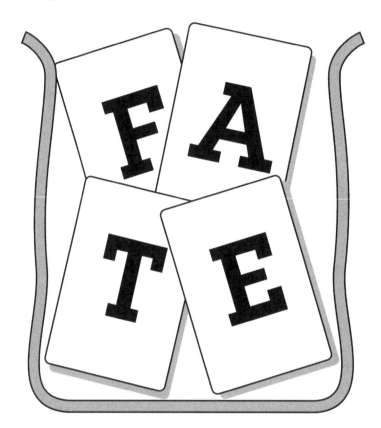

On the way in to the youth club you pick three letters from the bag and write them down in the order you pick them.

If your selection makes a word you get in for free.

Otherwise you have to pay your entrance fee.

1 What are the chances of you getting in for free?

Show all your working.

2 What would your chances be of getting in for free if you could re-arrange your letters after picking them?

Laura says: *'When I play a game using two fair dice, why is it that I always seem to get more threes and fours than elevens and twelves?'*

As if to prove her point, Laura has just thrown a total of four!

Activity

Perform an experiment to see if this is the case.

Try to give an explanation of your findings.

What would Laura usually get if she subtracted the lower score from the higher on the dice instead of adding them together?

Perform an experiment to see if your answer is correct.

This graph shows the **range** in the **temperature** in Miami each month.

For example, in January the temperature ranges from 17°C to 24°C.

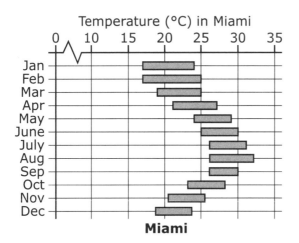

Miami

a In which month does Miami have the **smallest range** in temperature? *1 mark*

b In **July**, the **range** in the temperature in Miami is **5°**.

There are **five** other months in which the range in the temperature is 5°.

Which five months are they? *2 marks*

c This graph shows the range in the temperature in Orlando each month.

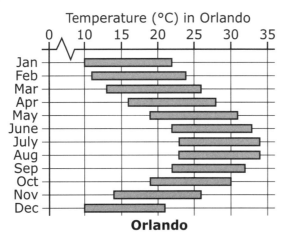

Orlando

In which **three** months is the **maximum** temperature in **Miami** **greater** than the maximum temperature in Orlando? *1 mark*

a   A bag has **20** cubes in it. **6** of the cubes are green.

You take one cube out of the bag at random.

Which values below show the **probability** that you take out a cube that is green?

Write down the correct **four** values.

$\frac{6}{14}$ 30%   0.6 $\frac{3}{10}$

6% $\frac{3}{5}$ $\frac{6}{20}$ 0.03

0.3 $\frac{6}{10}$ 60% $\frac{6}{26}$

2 marks

b   A box has **20** counters in it. **11** of the counters are red.

You take one counter out of the box at random.

What is the probability that the counter you take out is **not** red?

i   Write your answer as a **fraction**.   *1 mark*

ii   Now write your answer as a **percentage**.   *1 mark*

1 A magic square is one in which the total of each row, column or diagonal
is exactly the same.

$x + 2y + z$	x	$x + y + 2z$
$x + 2z$	$z + y + z$	$z + 2y$
$x + y$	$x + 2y + 2z$	$x + z$

Is this square magic when:

a $x = 7$, $y = 5$ and $z = 4$?

b $x = 3$, $y = 2$ and $z = {}^-2$?

2 Evaluate each expression for the values given:

a $a + 5b - 3c$ when $a = 10$, $b = 6$, $c = 4$

b $x^2 + 2x - y$ when $x = 12$, $y = 5$

c $4x + 2x$ when $x = 100$

d $p^2 - q^2 + pq$ when $p = 6$, $q = 7$

e $25 - 3k$ when $k = 9$

f $6(a - 2b) - c$ when $a = 15$, $b = 6$, $c = {}^-4$

g $6m^2 + 2m$ when $m = 4$

h n^3 when $n = 6$

3 Which value would you need on a dice to make each expression

a as large as possible   **b** as small as possible?

$30 - 4d$	$\frac{1}{2}(3d^2)$	$(d - d^2)^2$

1 ◆ Take a 3 × 3 square and select any four numbers, to enter into the corner squares:

3		7
4		8

◆ Follow this pattern of addition to get a centre total:

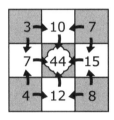

◆ The centre total here is 44.

a Try different sets of numbers.

What is the smallest/largest centre total you can make?

Does it make a difference if you put the same numbers in a different order?

b What happens with equal numbers? Or consecutive numbers?

c Can you predict the central total by using only the starting numbers?

d Use algebra to confirm your findings.

2 Test these statements with numbers and try to confirm your findings using algebra:

a When you add the house numbers of three consecutive houses, you always get a multiple of 3.

b When you add five consecutive numbers, the answer is always ten more than five lots of the smallest one.

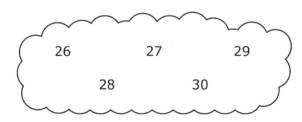

1 In this magic square each row, column and diagonal adds to give $3x + 3y + 3z$.

Devise your own 3×3 magic square.

$x + 2y + z$	x	$x + y + 2z$
$x + 2z$	$x + y + z$	$x + 2y$
$x + y$	$x + 2y + 2z$	$x + z$

2 Write simplified expressions for the perimeters of the following shapes.

a

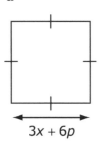

$3x + 6p$

b

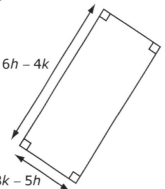

$6h - 4k$

$8k - 5h$

c

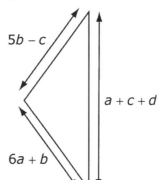

$5b - c$

$a + c + d$

$6a + b$

d

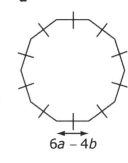

$6a - 4b$

3 In an algebragon, the expression in a square is the sum of the expressions in the two circles either side of it.

What are the missing expressions here?

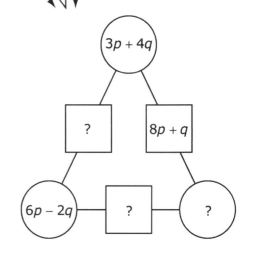

$3p + 4q$

? $8p + q$

$6p - 2q$? ?

◆ Copy the following grid.

◆ In each square, decide if the expression can be simplified.

◆ If so, simplify it as fully as possible.

◆ If not, shade it with a pencil and reveal a hidden message.

◆ The first one has been done to start you off.

$3x + 5x = 8x$	$5p + 3q - 4p$	$a \times b \times c$	$6b + 11b - 7b$	$4k \times 3$
$\dfrac{15k}{5}$	$4p \times 5q$	$7p \div 7$	$\dfrac{6b}{36}$	$4a \times 10c$
$a + b$	$\dfrac{144p}{12}$	$3 + 2x^2$	$8c + 10 - 2c + 3$	$3h + 5$
$p + 6$	$8j + 4k$	$6z - 2p$	$w \times w$	$14 - 3p$
$x + \dfrac{3}{2}$	$6q + 3w - q + 5w$	$10 + \dfrac{x}{2}$	$\dfrac{6ab}{3}$	$abcd$
$m + m$	$abc + cba$	$\dfrac{9q^2}{3q}$	$11pe \times 4d$	$5x + 8y + 2x + 10y$
$^-4b + 10b$	$\dfrac{4xy}{2y}$	$6x - 20 + 3x$	$\dfrac{54ax}{27x}$	$7xy - 3xy$
$10b^2 + 3b^2 + b$	$4c \times 3c$	$5cd \times 2pq$	$3m^2 \times m$	$m^3 + m^3$
$3m^2 + m^2$	$2x \times 5x \times 3x$	$\dfrac{6a^2b}{2a}$	$5k \times 2k^2$	$9 - 2y + 6 - 8y$

1   A formula to find the size of each angle in a regular polygon with n sides is:

$$A = 180 - \frac{360}{n}$$

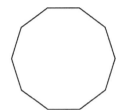

A = size of angle (degrees)

n = number of sides

Use the formula to find the size of an angle in a regular decagon.

2   A holiday is paid for by making an initial deposit of £50 and then paying £30 a month for 10 months.

   a   How much has been paid altogether after 4 months?

   b   Find a formula for the amount P paid after n months.

3   **a**   The time needed to cook a chicken is 40 minutes for each kilogram, plus an extra 20 minutes.

      Write a formula connecting T (time) and W (weight in kg).

   b   If a chicken takes 5 hours to cook, how heavy is it?

4   The diagram shows a pattern of matches with two rows.

The formula for the number of matches (M) in a diagram with R rows is given by:

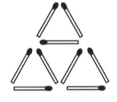

$$M = \tfrac{1}{2}\,(3R^2 + 3R)$$

Use the formula to find the number of matches needed for a diagram with 10 rows.

5   Derive a formula for the quantities described.

   a   The number of shaded tiles in this sequence of patterns.

Pattern 1   Pattern 2   Pattern 3

   b   The number of patio tiles T needed to surround a garden measuring 3 metres by P metres. Each tile measures 0.5 metres by 0.5 metres.

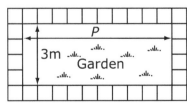

Ali, Barry and Cindy each have a bag of counters.

They do not know how many counters are in each bag.

They know that   Barry has **two more** counters than Ali

Cindy has **four times as many** counters as Ali.

a Ali calls the number of counters in her bag **a**.

Write **expressions using a** to show the number of counters in Barry's bag and in Cindy's bag.   *1 mark*

b Barry calls the number of counters in his bag **b**.

Write **expressions using b** to show the number of counters in Ali's bag and in Cindy's bag.   *2 marks*

c Cindy calls the number of counters in her bag **c**.

Which of the expressions below shows the number of counters in **Barry's** bag?

Write down the correct one.

$4c + 2$ $4c - 2$ $\dfrac{c}{4} + 2$

$\dfrac{c}{4} - 2$ $\dfrac{c + 2}{4}$ $\dfrac{c - 2}{4}$

1 mark

Here are some algebra cards:

| $n \div 2$ | | $2 + n$ |

| $n + 2$ | | n^2 |

| | n | | $2n$ |

| $n - 2$ | | $n + n$ |

| | n^3 | | $2n - n$ |

a One of the cards will always give the same answer as
Which card is it?

$$\frac{n}{2}$$

1 mark

b One of the cards will always give the same answer as
Which card is it?

$$n \times n$$

1 mark

c **Two** of the cards will always give the same answer as
Which cards are they?

$$2 \times n$$

2 marks

d Write a **new** card which will always give the same
answer as

$$3n + 2n$$

1 mark

Example

Find the unknown angle a.
Show all your working.

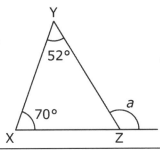

$\angle XZY = 180° - 52° - 70°$

$= 58°$ (angles in a triangle)

$a = 180° - 58°$

$= 122°$ (angles on a straight line)

In questions 1 to 6, find the unknown angle and show all your working clearly.

None of the shapes are drawn accurately.

1 Find BĈD.

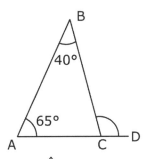

2 Find angle x.

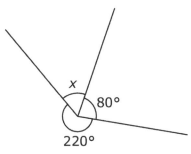

3 Find AB̂C.

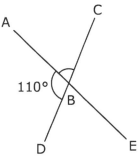

4 Find QR̂S.

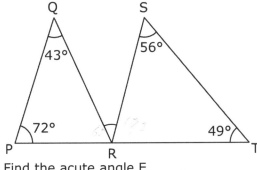

5 Find AD̂E.

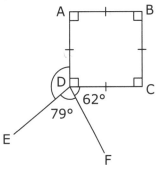

6 Find the acute angle E.

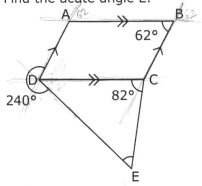

In the example and question 1, what do you notice if you add together the angles given?

45

1 **a** Which pair of sides are parallel in trapezium PQRS?

   b Which pair of sides are perpendicular?

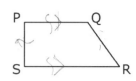

2 Copy this diagram and label
all the angles that are equal to *x*.

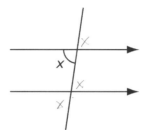

3 Copy this diagram and label any
angles that are not equal to *a*.

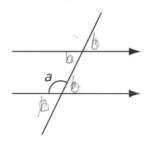

4 Copy the diagrams and label the corresponding angles to those shown.

a 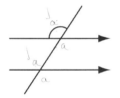 **b** 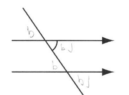 **c**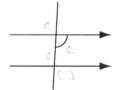

5 Copy the diagrams and label the alternate angles to those shown.

a 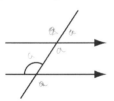 **b** 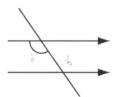 **c**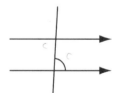

6 Calculate the unknown angles.

a 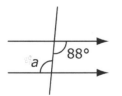 **b** 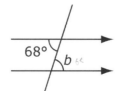 **c**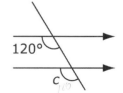

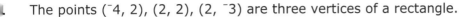

S2.3HW   Coordinates and shapes

1. The points (⁻4, 2), (2, 2), (2, ⁻3) are three vertices of a rectangle.

   Write down the coordinates of the fourth vertex.

   Find the area and perimeter of the rectangle.

2. Plot these three points: (2, 3), (⁻1, 2), (2, ⁻1). What fourth point will make:

   a   a kite

   b   a parallelogram

   c   an arrowhead?

   In each case, explain how you chose your fourth coordinate.

   d   Is it possible to make a rectangle? Explain your answer.

3. The points (⁻5, 2), (3, 2), (3, 3) are three vertices of a rectangle.

   a   Write down the coordinates of the fourth vertex.

   b   Find the area and perimeter of the rectangle.

4. The points (⁻3, 3), (⁻3, ⁻2) are two vertices of a right-angled isosceles triangle.

   a   Write down the coordinates of the third vertex. Is there more than one vertex
   you could use?

   b   Find the area of the triangle.

5. The points (⁻3, 3), (⁻3, ⁻3) are two vertices of a square.

   a   Write down the coordinates of the third and fourth vertices. Are there different
   vertices you could use?

   b   Find the area and perimeter of the square.

6. Draw a pair of axes labelled from ⁻6 to ⁺6. On your axes draw:

   a   a square

   b   a rectangle

   c   a right-angled triangle

   Write down the coordinates of your shapes.

Level 5

Look at these angles.

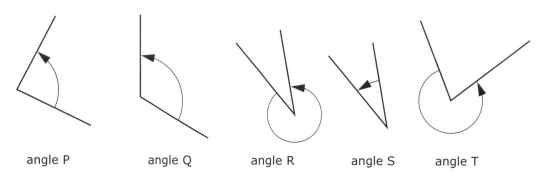

| angle P | angle Q | angle R | angle S | angle T |

a   One of the angles measures **120°**. Write down its letter.   *1 mark*

b   Make a drawing to show an angle of **157°**.
      Label the angle 157°.   *2 marks*

c   15 pupils measured two angles. Here are their results.

Angle A

Angle measured as	Number of pupils
36°	1
37°	2
38°	10
39°	2

Angle B

Angle measured as	Number of pupils
45°	5
134°	3
135°	4
136°	3

Use the results to decide what each angle is most likely to
measure.

i   What size is angle **A**? How did you decide?   *1 mark*

ii   What size is angle **B**? How did you decide?   *1 mark*

─── Level 6

Kay is drawing shapes on her computer.

a She wants to draw this triangle. She needs to know angles *a*, *b* and *c*.

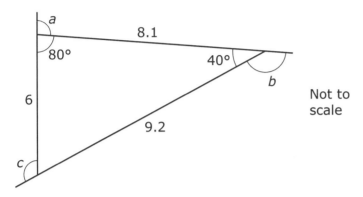

Not to scale

Calculate angles *a*, *b* and *c*.   *3 marks*

b Kay draws a rhombus.

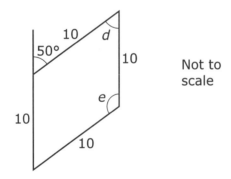

Not to scale

Calculate angles *d* and *e*.   *2 marks*

c Kay types the instructions to draw a regular pentagon:

> **repeat 5 [forward 10, left turn 72]**

Copy and complete these instructions to draw a regular hexagon:

> repeat 6 [forward 10, left turn ....]   *1 mark*

1   Tony and Tim want to try and predict who will win the premier league this season.
They study the league table from last year.

What sort of data are they studying?

Give three reasons why this data is not always suitable.

For example, players may be transferred between teams over the summer so the teams are not the same.

2   Retowners, a sweet manufacturer, wants to produce a new pack of jelly sweets.

What sort of data should they collect?

Where would they obtain this data?

3   Mobs-R-Us manufactures mobile phones.

They want to design and make a new phone that would be popular amongst the ten to thirteen age group.

How could they use secondary data to help in the design of the phone?

How could they use primary data?

What would be the advantage of using primary data to help their design?

What could be a problem with trying to find primary data?

A primary school wants to find out if parents and children at their school would be interested in setting up a walking bus.

Your task is to write a short questionnaire and design a data collection sheet to collect the information.

Here are some questions you could consider:

Walk to School Questionnaire

1. Do you walk to school?   Every day ☐ Sometimes ☐ Never ☐

2. How long does it take you to get to school? _____

3. How far do you live

   from school?   C B A ✕ School

4. Would you use a walking

   bus to get to school?

Also, you could think about other questions to find out:

◆ How many students live near each other?

◆ Is the journey difficult to walk?

◆ What do students think about the use of cars and other environmental issues?

◆ Would students feel safe in a walking bus?

> Remember to design your collection sheet after you know what questions you will ask. Give yourself enough space to write in all the information you will need.

1   Fifty children took part in a cross-country race.

Their times were recorded to the nearest minute.

20	27	23	45	42
31	39	42	43	39
53	48	42	42	39
48	47	32	42	40
24	49	33	47	44
37	39	36	44	30
31	36	27	36	35
41	46	50	52	28
43	37	42	30	28
43	29	39	41	32

Complete this frequency table, using seven equal class intervals, to collate these data.

Time	Tally	Frequency

2   The opening batsman in a cricket team scored these numbers of runs in each innings he played during one season.

32	43	56	33	12
45	0	38	42	18
26	15	27	24	10
0	29	54	59	4
24	38	52	0	2
8	6	43	21	57

Draw a frequency table, using equal class intervals, to collate these data.

1 This frequency table shows the time (in minutes) taken by 50 children to complete a cross-country race.

Draw a frequency diagram to represent the data.

Time	Tally	Frequency
20 – 24	|||	3
25 – 29	ЖЖ	5
30 – 34	ЖЖ ||	7
35 – 39	ЖЖ ЖЖ		11
40 – 44	ЖЖ ЖЖ ||||	14
45 – 49	ЖЖ ||	7
50 – 54	|||	3

2 Draw a pie chart to represent this data describing the number of students living in the same street. You will need to think carefully about how best to divide up your pie.

Number of pupils	Frequency
0	2
1	5
2	7
3	12
4	8
5	3

Which chart best displays the data – a pie chart or a line graph?

Give a reason for your answer.

1 The frequency diagram shows the distribution of the ages of teachers at Maypole Primary School.

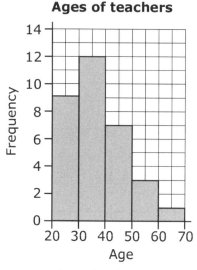

Ages of teachers

a How many teachers were at the school?

b How many teachers were in their twenties?

c How many teachers were at least 40 years old?

d Laura stated that the youngest teacher at the school was 20 years old.
Can this conclusion be made? Give a reason for your answer.

2 Maypole Secondary School conducted a survey to find out the usual way their Year 7 pupils travel to school each day. This composite bar chart shows their findings.

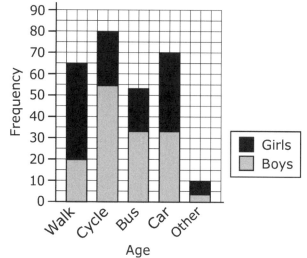

Ways that Year 7 pupils travel to school

Summarise the differences in the way boys and girls travel to Maypole Secondary School.

These pie charts show some information about the ages of people in Greece and in Ireland.

There are about 10 million people in Greece, and there are about 3.5 million people in Ireland.

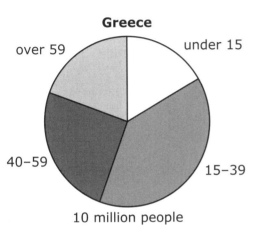

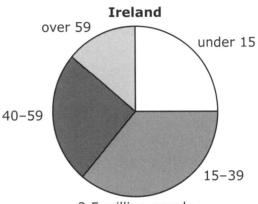

a Roughly what **percentage** of people in **Greece** are aged **40–59**?   *1 mark*

b There are about **10 million** people in Greece.

Use your percentage from part **a** to work out roughly **how many** people in Greece are aged **40–59**.   *1 mark*

c Dewi says: *'The charts show that there are **more** people **under 15** in **Ireland** than in **Greece**.'*

Dewi is **wrong**. Explain why the charts do **not** show this.

1 mark

d There are about 60 million people in the UK.

The table shows roughly what percentage of people in the UK are of different ages.

under 15	15–39	40–59	over 59
20%	35%	25%	20%

Draw a pie-chart to show the information in the table.
Label each section of your pie chart clearly with the **ages**.

You could start by by dividing your pie chart into tenths.

3 marks

A teacher asked two different classes: *'What type of book is your favourite?'*

a   Results from **class A** (total 20 pupils):

Type of book	Frequency
Crime	3
Non-fiction	13
Fantasy	4

Copy and complete the pie chart
to show this information.
*Show your working and draw
your angles accurately.*

2 marks

b   The pie chart below shows the results
from all of **class B**.

Each pupil had only one vote.

The sector for **non-fiction**
represents **11 pupils**.

How many pupils are in class B?

Show your working.

2 marks

1 Copy and complete:

a 100 × 78 = __   **b** 9 ÷ 10 = __   **c** __ × 100 = 8900   **d** 9.4 ÷ 100 = __

2 What have each of these numbers been multiplied by to become the numbers in the brackets?

a 14 (140)   **b** 160 (16 000)   **c** 2 (200)

3 What have each of these numbers been divided by to become the numbers in the brackets?

a 14 (140)   **b** 160 (16 000)   **c** 2 (200)

4 Work out:

a 6 × 0.1   **b** 7 ÷ 0.01   **c** 3 × 0.01   **d** 2 ÷ 0.1

5 Complete these:

a _____ × 0.01 = 0.8   **b** 9.43 ÷ _____ = 943

c 661 ÷ 0.01 = _____   **d** _____ × 0.01 = 2.22

6 Change these into cm^2:

a 400 m^2 **b** 60 m^2 **c** 0.7 m^2

7 Change these into mm^2:

a 6 000 000 cm^2 **b** 6000 cm^2 **c** 0.5 m^2

8 Change these into mm^2:

a 80 cm^2 **b** 560 000 cm^2 **c** 1.2 cm^2

9 Which is longer: 10 rods of length 0.21 m or one piece from a 2000 cm rod cut into 10 pieces? Explain your answer.

10 Work out:

a 0.5 × 0.7   **b** 0.6 ÷ 0.05   **c** 4.5 × 0.2   **d** 3.7 × 0.08

11 Show, with the help of a diagram, why 100 cm^2 is not equal to 1 m^2.

12 Convert these areas in m^2 into mm^2.
 (**Hint:** You may find it useful to convert into cm^2 first.)

a 5 m^2 **b** 0.4 m^2 **c** 0.006 m^2 **d** 0.31 m^2

Make a set of 12 loop cards which will help you practise the order of operations.

For example:

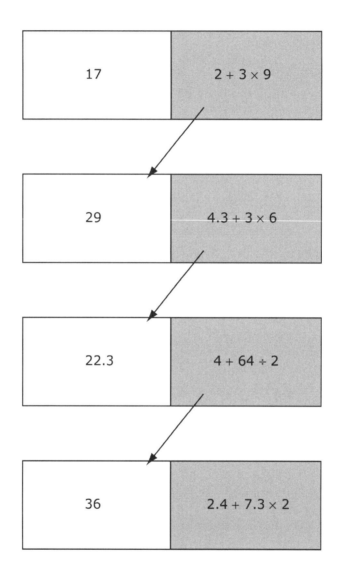

Make sure that the question on your last card has an answer of 17.

You can calculate complicated problems by partitioning.

For example:

To calculate 45×31

$45 \times 31 = 40 \times 31 + 5 \times 31$

$40 \times 31 = 4 \times 10 \times 31$

$\qquad = 4 \times 310$

$\qquad = 1240$

$5 \times 31 = \frac{1}{2} \times 10 \times 31$

$\qquad = 310 \div 2$

$\qquad = 155$

So $45 \times 31 = 1240 + 155 = 1395$

Alternatively, you can say:

$45 \times 31 = 45 \times 30 + 45 \times 1$

$\qquad = 45 \times 3 \times 10 + 45$

$\qquad = 135 \times 10 + 45$

$\qquad = 1350 + 45$

$\qquad = 1395$

Design a poster showing how to calculate 97×17 using different methods.

For each of these questions:

a Estimate the answer:

for example $4.1 \times 3.53 \approx 4 \times 3.5 = 14$

b Calculate the exact answer:

for example:

×	300	50	3
40	12000	2000	120
1	300	50	3

```
12 000
 2 000
   120
   300
    50
     3
_____
14 473
```

So $4.1 \times 3.53 = 14.473$

1 435×23 **2** 56×745

3 98×362 **4** 834×27

5 42×871 **6** 39×835

7 45×102 **8** 73×555

9 4.8×3.4 **10** 8.3×9.3

11 5.5×1.9 **12** 1.1×1.7

13 5.2×9.2 **14** 54.6×8.3

15 3.6×91.2 **16** 46.3×6.7

17 2.65×4.6 **18** 39.2×6.2

19 0.05×0.123 **20** 4.3×0.781

This information shows the number of children in Blob Top School for Super Intelligent Humanoids:

Total number of students	721
Year 7	151
Year 8	149
Year 9	140
Year 10	144
Year 11	137
Number of teachers	38

Use this information to answer these questions:

1   If every Year 7 child had 23 cats, how many cats would that be altogether?

2   If each of these cats weighed 935 g, what would their total weight be (in grams or kilograms)?

3   The mother of every Year 10 child goes to a slimming club. In a particular week they all lose 95 g. How much did they lose altogether?

4   The cats of the Year 7 students each eat food costing £3.46 per week. How much does it cost one pupil per week?

5   Add together the total number of students in Years 7, 8 and 9.

6   In Year 9 there are 85 girls. Each girl receives, on average, £6.80 per month spending money. How much, in total, is this per month?

7   If it costs £9.15 for each Year 11 student to enter an Art competition, and there are 80 girls in Year 11, how much does it cost to enter all Year 11 boys?

8   Every teacher at this school begins each term with a pencil measuring 9.46 cm. If the teachers put their pencils end to end, what would the total length of the pencils be?

9   If each pencil costs £0.26, what is the total cost of the pencils?

To calculate 62.1 ÷ 0.9 you:

◆   multiply both numbers by 10 to make the divisor a whole number
◆   use long division.

62.1 × 10 = 621

0.9 × 10 = 9

Now calculate 621 ÷ 9

Use long division:

$$9\overline{)621}$$

    $\underline{540}$ 60×9
    81
    $\underline{81}$ $\underline{9×9}$
     0   69×9

So 621 ÷ 9 = 69
and 62.1 ÷ 0.9 = 69

Show how you would work out:

a   35.14 ÷ 0.7

b   72.36 ÷ 0.9

c   67.5 ÷ 0.03

Dividing with remainders

1 Orace the octopus is 2000 years old. Only 7 of his legs give the correct answer when the numbers on his 'joints' are applied to his age.

For example, the leftmost leg: 2000 ÷ 0.1 × 3.7 = 74 000 (Correct!)

a Use estimation to decide which leg has a false answer.

Show your working.

b What is the correct answer for the leg with the false answer?

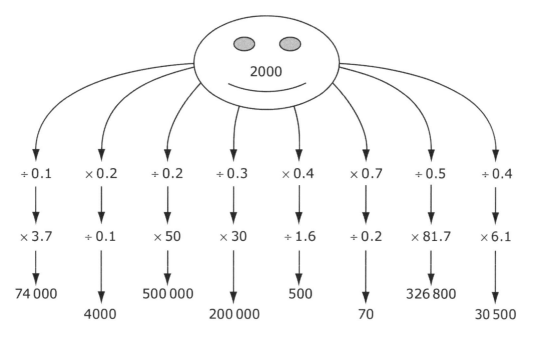

2 After their match, twelve members of a football squad go out to celebrate their win.

The bill comes to £316.42. They split it equally between them.

How much do they each owe?

3 657 ÷ 9 = 73

Write down the answers to these questions:

a 657 ÷ 0.9 =

b 6.57 ÷ 9 =

c 6.57 ÷ 0.09 =

d 657 ÷ 0.73 =

e 65.7 ÷ 7.3 =

Be a publisher!

The students at To The Point School think that the 'how to use your calculator' handbooks that come with new calculators should win a prize for 'gobbledigook'!

Produce an easy to understand plain English version of how to use the keys on your calculator.

Points to consider

◆ Your target audience is 11/12 year olds, not university professors.

Your guide should:

◆ Explain how to use these keys:

◆ Explain how to interpret the display when doing calculations in different units, especially time.

◆ Say what common mistakes can be made.

---

a   Robert and Gwen must put 63 tins of food into a lift.

Each tin weighs **840 g**.

Work out the total weight of the **63** tins in grams.

*Remember to write down enough working to show you
have not used a calculator.*   *2 marks*

b   In the lift there is a sign.

It shows the greatest load that the lift can carry safely.

Look at the total weight of the 63 tins, which you worked
out in part **a**.

Is it safe to carry the 63 tins together in the lift?

Give a reason for your answer.   *1 mark*

> **Greatest load
> 50 kg**

c   Robert and Gwen must put the tins into a cupboard.

All the tins are the same size.

Gwen has measured the height of a **tin**. It is **14cm.**

Robert has measured the height of the **cupboard**.
It is **1.24m**.

How many **layers** of tins can they keep in the cupboard?

*Remember to write down enough working to show you
have not used a calculator.*   *3 marks*

---

a   Look at these numbers.

| 1^6 | 2^5 | 3^4 | 4^3 | 5^2 | 6^1 |

i   Which is the **largest**?   *1 mark*

ii   Which is equal to 9^2?   *1 mark*

b   Which **two** of the numbers below are **not** square numbers?

| 2^4 | 2^5 | 2^6 | 2^7 | 2^8 |

1 mark

Copy and complete the crossword using the clues given.

1			2		
3					
		4			5
	6				
7				8	
			9		

ACROSS

1　The lowest common multiple of 6 and 15

2　A square number between 150 and 180

3　The highest common factors of 48 and 120

4　A square number between 1100 and 1200

6　The number which can be written as $2^3 \times 3^2 \times 5$

7　The last multiple of 193 before 1000

9　The first multiple of 11 without a repeated digit

DOWN

1　A multiple of 17 that is a palindrome

2　The smallest prime number over 100

4　A common multiple of 5 and 11 between 140 and 200

5　The only common multiple of 7 and 9 under 100

6　The biggest factor of 728, except itself

8　A prime number under 100 whose digit sum is 7

1   Match each sequence **a** to **i** with a formula A to I:

Sequence	Formula
a 8, 16, 24, 32, ...	A $T(n) = n^2 - 1$
b $\frac{1}{1}, \frac{1}{4}, \frac{1}{9}, \frac{1}{16}, \frac{1}{25}, ...$	B $T(n) = 8n$
c 9, 14, 19, 24, 29, ...	C $T(n) = \dfrac{n}{n+1}$
d 2, 8, 18, 32, 50, ...	D $T(n) = 5n + 4$
e 0, 3, 8, 15, 24, ...	E $T(n) = \dfrac{1}{3n}$
f 2, ⁻1, ⁻4, ⁻7, ⁻10, ...	F $T(n) = 6n - 1$
g $\frac{1}{3}, \frac{1}{6}, \frac{1}{9}, \frac{1}{12}, \frac{1}{15}, ...$	G $T(n) = 2n^2$
h 5, 11, 17, 23, 29, ...	H $T(n) = \dfrac{1}{n^2}$
i $\frac{1}{2}, \frac{2}{3}, \frac{3}{4}, \frac{4}{5}, \frac{5}{6}, ...$	I $T(n) = 5 - 3n$

2   Write a formula for each of these sequences:

a   8, 12, 16, 20, 24, ...

b   3, 16, 29, 42, 55, ...

c   1, 4, 9, 16, 25, ...

d   1, 8, 27, 64, 125, ...

e $\frac{1}{2}, \frac{1}{4}, \frac{1}{6}, \frac{1}{8}, \frac{1}{10}, ...$

f $\frac{2}{1}, \frac{2}{4}, \frac{2}{9}, \frac{2}{16}, \frac{2}{25}, ...$

g $\frac{2}{3}, \frac{3}{4}, \frac{4}{5}, \frac{5}{6}, \frac{6}{7}, ...$

A3.3HW Patterns in numbers

For each diagram in questions 1 to 3:

a copy and complete the table of values

b obtain a formula to connect the two quantities

c use the diagrams to explain why the formula works

1

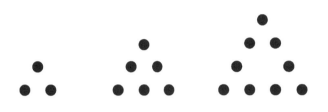

Pattern number n	Number of dots d
1	
2	
3	
4	

2

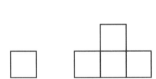

Height h	Number of tiles n
1	
2	
3	
4	

3

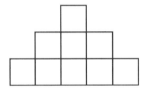

June

M	Tu	W	Th	F	Sa	Su
					1	2
3	4	5	6	7	8	9
10	11	12	13	14	15	16
17	18	19	20	21	22	23
24	25	26	27	28	29	30

Date d	Number below in calendar n
1	
2	
3	
4	

1 For each of the function machines:
- compile a table of values for the inputs and outputs
- find the rule and express it as a mapping $n \rightarrow$

a

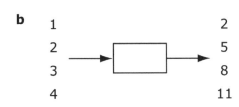

1	3
2	6
3	9
4	12

b

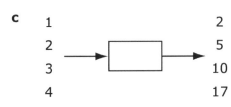

1	2
2	5
3	8
4	11

c

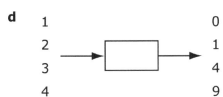

1	2
2	5
3	10
4	17

d

1	0
2	1
3	4
4	9

2 For each equation:
- compile a table of values for x and y
- choose integer values of x from ⁻2 to 2

a $y = 2x - 1$

b $y = 5x + 2$

c $y = (3x - 2)^2$

d $y = \frac{5}{2}x^2 + 1$

1 For each equation copy and complete the table.

Draw a set of axes labelled from ⁻10 to ⁺10.

Plot the coordinates, join and extend with your ruler.

Label the graph with its equation.

a $y = x + 3$

x	1	2	3
y			

b $y = 2x + 1$

x	1	2	3
y			

c $y = 3x - 4$

x	1	2	3
y			

d $x + y = 10$

x	1	2	3
y			

2 Pick an equation from Box A, a shape for this graph from Box B and a coordinate that would lie on this graph from Box C.

Box A

Box B

Box C

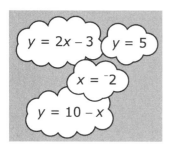
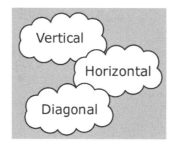
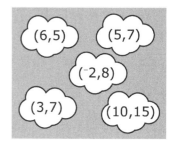

1 Does the straight line $y = x - 3$ cut through the point (10, 10)?

Explain your answer.

2 Write down the equations of three graphs that cut through the point (3, 7).

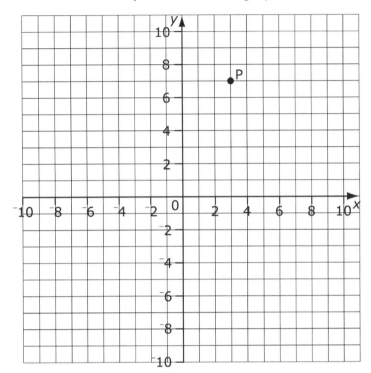

3 Where do the following graphs intersect?

You may wish to sketch them.

a $x = 3$ and $y = 5$

b $y = {}^-2$ and $x = 7$

c $x = 4$ and $y = x + 3$

4 Name a graph which:

a is parallel to $y = 3x$

b is steeper than $y = 2x$

c is horizontal

d is not a straight line

e cuts the y-axis at (0, 4)

f passes through (1, 4) and (2, 3)

The grid shows the first eight lines of a spiral pattern.

The spiral pattern starts at the point marked ■.

a Copy and continue the spiral by drawing the **next four lines** on a square grid.

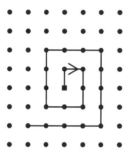

1 mark

b The table shows the length of each line.

line number	length
1	1
2	1
3	2
4	2
5	3
6	3
7	4
8	4
9	5

The rule for finding the length of **odd** numbered lines is:

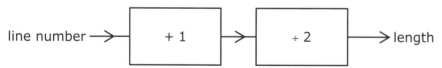

What is the length of line number **23**? *1 mark*

c Copy this diagram and fill in the box to show the rule for finding the length of **even** numbered lines.

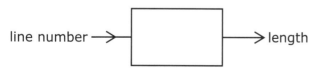

1 mark

d What is the length of line number **18**? *1 mark*

Look at this diagram:

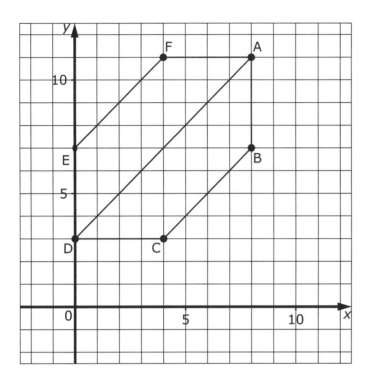

a   The line through points A and F has the equation $y = 11$.

    What is the equation of the line through points **A** and **B**?

1 mark

b   The line through points A and D has the equation $y = x + 3$.

    What is the equation of the line through points **F** and **E**?

1 mark

c   What is the equation of the line through points **B** and **C**?

1 mark

1   Paul is solving this angle problem.

He thinks that x is 40 degrees.

How can you tell this is a wrong answer? What should the answer be?

2   Sally is solving this angle problem.

She thinks that x is 100 degrees.

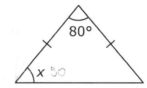

How can you tell this is the wrong answer? What should the answer be?

3   Samad is solving this angle problem.

He thinks that x is 120 degrees.

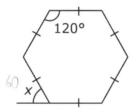

How can you tell this is the wrong answer? What should the answer be?

4   Roxanne is solving this angle problem.

She thinks that x is 25 degrees.

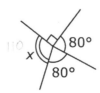

How can you tell this is the wrong answer? What should the answer be?

Here is a regular hexagon.

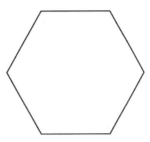

The hexagon can be split into four triangles.

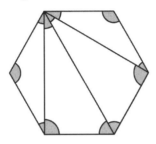

◆   The sum of the interior angles of each triangle is 180°.

◆   So the sum of the interior angles of the hexagon is:

$$4 \times 180° = 720°$$

◆   There are six equal angles so each angle is:

$$720° \div 6 = 120°$$

Activity

Using the same method, calculate the size of an interior angle of:

a   a regular pentagon

b   a regular octagon

c   a regular decagon

1   Construct △PQR where PQ = 5.5 cm, ∠P = 42°, ∠Q = 38°.

Measure QR, PR and angle R.

2   Construct △ABC where AB = 6.3 cm, AC = 5.2 cm and ∠A = 42°.
Measure ∠B, ∠C and BC.

3   Construct △XYZ where XY = 5 cm, YZ = 12 cm, XZ = 13 cm.
Measure ∠X, ∠Y and ∠Z.

4   Construct △RST where RS = 10 cm, ST = 4 cm, TR = 5 cm.
What problems did you find? Explain your answer.

5   Construct △EFG where EF = 8 cm, ∠F = 100°, ∠E = 95°.
What problems did you find? Explain your answer.

1 **a** Using a protractor, draw these angles:

  i   40°   **ii**   100°   **iii**   80°

  b Bisect each angle in part **a**.

2 Draw a line PQ = 5 cm.

  Construct the perpendicular bisector of PQ and label the midpoint of PQ as X.

3 **a** Using a protractor, draw these angles:

  i   200°   **ii**   300°

  b Bisect each angle in part **a** as shown.

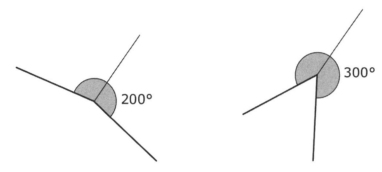

4 Draw an equilateral triangle PQR where PQ = 12 cm.
  Bisect each side.
  Label the point of intersection X as shown.
  Using X as the centre, draw a circle inside ΔPQR as shown. This circle is called the **incircle**.

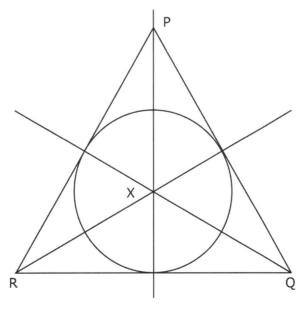

1 Draw accurately the net of a triangular prism, where:

- ◆ the triangle is right angled with sides 4.5 cm, 6 cm and 7.5 cm
- ◆ the length of the prism is 5.5 cm.

2 Sketch the solid you have just made.

3 How many edges, vertices and faces does your shape have?

4 Draw accurately its plan, front elevation and side elevation.

5 Find the surface area of your solid.

Challenge

Here is the net of an octahedron.

Either

- ◆ Copy it, cut it out and make the shape by gluing the tabs

or

- ◆ Sketch the shape of the 3D solid.

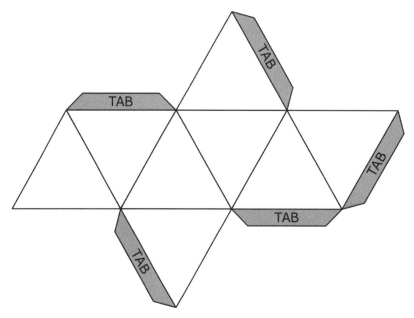

Here is a plan of a ferry crossing:

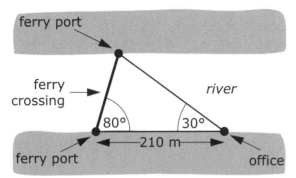

Not drawn accurately

a   Copy and complete the accurate scale drawing of the ferry crossing below.

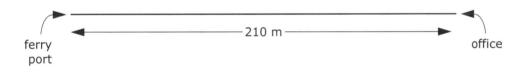

2 marks

b   What is the length of the ferry crossing in cm on **your** diagram?

1 mark

c   The scale is **1 cm** to **20 m**. Work out the length of the real ferry crossing.

*Show your working, and **write the units with your answer**.*

2 marks

a Any quadrilateral can be split into 2 triangles.

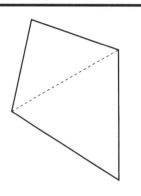
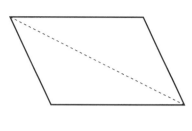

Explain how you know that the angles inside a **quadrilateral** add up to 360°.

1 mark

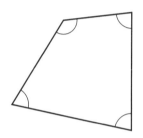

b What do the angles inside a **pentagon** add up to?　　　*1 mark*

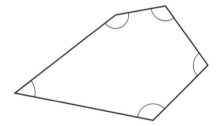

c What do the angles inside a **heptagon** (7 sided shape) add up to?
Show your working.　　　*2 marks*

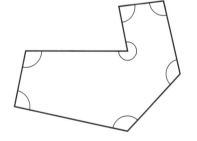

1 Fergie has 50 sweets.

He offers his four friends a share of his sweets.

They must choose which share to take:

$\frac{1}{5}$, 22%, 0.3 or $\frac{7}{25}$

a Which share is the largest?

b Which share is the smallest?

c Put the shares in order of size.

2 What number is halfway between:

a $\frac{2}{3}$ and 0.6

b 45% and 0.87

c 0.12 and $\frac{1}{10}$

d $\frac{3}{8}$ and $\frac{3}{10}$?

3 **a** Find the decimal equivalent of $\frac{1}{9}$.

b Use your answers to write down $\frac{2}{9}$, $\frac{3}{9}$, $\frac{4}{9}$, $\frac{5}{9}$, $\frac{6}{9}$, $\frac{7}{9}$, $\frac{8}{9}$ and $\frac{9}{9}$ as decimals.

c What do you notice about $\frac{9}{9}$, after working it out this way?

1 Work out these amounts using a written method:

   a $\frac{3}{8}$ of £17

   b 0.35×25 cm

   c $\frac{19}{25}$ of 20 kg

2 For each part of question 1:

   i Rewrite the problem using a percentage.

   ii Work out the amount using a written method.

   iii Which form is easier to use? Give a reason for your answer.

3 Demonstrate two different methods of working out these calculations on paper:

   a 45% of £88

   b 35% of 6 kg

   c 90% of 50 cm

4 What percentage of:

   a 30 kg is 7.5 kg

   b 60 cm is 45 cm

   c £84 is £31.50

   d 78 litres is 52 litres?

1   The table shows the change in the price of two houses in a street.

	Number 23	Number 62
Price 1 year ago	£125,000	£235,000
Price now	£143,000	£221,000
% increase or decrease?		

Fill in the last row of the table by calculating the percentage increase or decrease in the price over the last year.

2   **Challenge**

A shop has 20% off all items in a sale.

a   The sale price of a TV is £360.

   What was the original price of the TV?

b   A games console is reduced by 20% and then reduced by a further 15%.
     It now costs £138.

   i   How much was the initial sale price?

   ii   What was the original price?

1 Here are two currency exchange rates:

£1 = €1.61   £1 = $1.55

a How many euros will you get for £15?

b A pair of jeans costs $26 in New York.

How many pounds sterling is this?

c A CD in the UK costs £13.

How much is this in US dollars?

d A CD in the US costs $13.

How much is this in pounds sterling?

e A railway ticket in France costs € 10.

How much is this in pounds sterling?

2 a 4 kg of potatoes cost £1.08.

How much does 7 kg of potatoes cost?

b On a map, a distance of 5 km is represented by 2 cm.

What length on the map would represent 9 km?

c Which is better value for money:

◆ a litre bottle of washing-up liquid costing 89p, or

◆ a 1.5 litre bottle of washing-up liquid costing £1.30?

Explain your choice.

3 Five kilograms is roughly equivalent to 11 pounds in weight.

a How many kilograms make 20 pounds?

b How many pounds are equivalent to 12 kilograms?

Give your answers to **a** and **b** to 1 decimal place.

c On graph paper, draw a conversion graph to show how to change kg to lb (make sure it includes up to 40 lb and 20 kg).

d Use your graph to find how many kg are equivalent to 32 lb.

1   In a particular year group there are 200 students.

40 of these students have fair hair.

Find the ratio of fair-haired students to students who do not have fair hair.

Give your answer in its simplest form.

2   To make biscuits, flour and butter are mixed in the ratio 15:7.

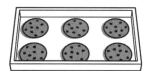

a   How much butter would be needed if you had 22.5 kg of flour?

b   How much flour would you need if you had 12 g of butter?
Give your answer to 1 dp.

3   Prakash, Rachel and James want to share £700 in the ratio 12:10:6.

How much will each person receive?

4   A map is drawn to a scale of 2 cm to 1 km.

a   Convert 1 km to centimetres.

b   Write the scale 2 cm to 1 km as a ratio in its simplest form.

a Nigel pours **1** carton of **apple** juice and **3** cartons of **orange** juice into a big jug.

What is the **ratio** of **apple** juice to **orange** juice in Nigel's jug?

apple juice : orange juice = _____ : _____   *1 mark*

b Lesley pours **1** carton of **apple** juice and **1**$\frac{1}{2}$ cartons of **orange** juice into another big jug.

What is the **ratio** of **apple** juice to **orange** juice in Lesley's jug?

apple juice : orange juice = _____ : _____   *1 mark*

c Tandi pours **1** carton of **apple** juice and **1** carton of **orange** juice into another big jug.

She wants only **half** as much **apple** juice as **orange** juice in her jug.

What should Tandi pour into her jug now?   *1 mark*

Level 6

a The label on yoghurt A shows this information.

> Yoghurt A   **125 g**
>
> Each 125g provides
>
> | | |
> |---|---|
> | Energy | 430 kJ |
> | Protein | 4.5 g |
> | Carbohydrate | 11.1 g |
> | Fat | 4.5 g |

How many grams of **protein** does **100g** of yoghurt provide?

Show your working.   *2 marks*

b The label on yoghurt B shows different information.

> Yoghurt B   **150 g**
>
> Each 150g provides
>
> | | |
> |---|---|
> | Energy | 339 kJ |
> | Protein | 6.6 g |
> | Carbohydrate | 13.1 g |
> | Fat | 0.2 g |

A boy eats the same amount of yoghurt A and yoghurt B.

Which yoghurt provides him with more **carbohydrate**?

Show your working.   *2 marks*

Copy out the crossword grid.

Solve the equations to complete the clues across and down.

1		■	**2**
3	■	**4**	
■	**5**		■
6		■	**7**

Across

1 $4x - 20 = 36$

3 $6 - x = {}^-2$

4 $2(x + 4) = 28$

5 $3x - 12 = 21$

6 $\dfrac{2(x - 3)}{3} = 16$

7 $6(x + 2) = 30$

Down

1 $\dfrac{(x + 3)}{7} = 3$

2 $2(s - 5) = 30$

4 $\dfrac{(3x - 5)}{4} = 7$

5 $\dfrac{3(x - 7)}{2} = 15$

Copy out the number grid carefully.

1	4	8	5	7
9	3	7	2	1
6	2	4	8	2
8	3	9	6	0

Solve these equations. If you are correct, you should find the answer in the grid.
Ring your answers in the grid.

1 $\dfrac{(3x - 60)}{5} = 60$

2 $2x - 8 = 18$

3 $4x - 6 = 2x + 12$

4 $2x + 12 = 3x - 27$

5 $8x - 56 = 3x + 49$

6 $12x - 1184 = 7x + 1976$

7 $2(x + 7) = 8(x - 2)$

8 $x + 10 = 2x - 37$

9 $\dfrac{x}{9} + 7 = 14$

10 $5x^2 + 5 = 250$

1 For each shape, write an expression for the shaded area using brackets.
Expand your brackets.

a

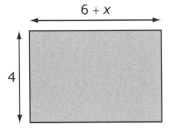

b

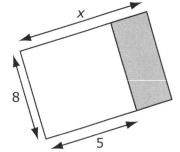

c

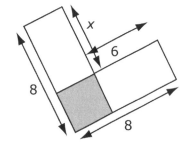

2 These expressions have already been expanded.

Copy and complete the expressions to show what they looked like with brackets.

a $4x + 18 = 2(2x + \underline{\quad})$

b $6x - 21 = 3(\underline{\quad} - \underline{\quad})$

c $y^2 - 3y = y(\underline{\quad} - \underline{\quad})$

d $10pq + 4q = 2q (\underline{\quad} + \underline{\quad})$

This map shows seven villages and the roads connecting them.

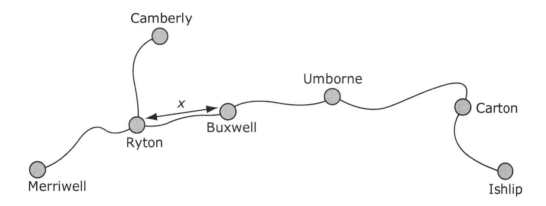

The distance from Ryton to Buxwell is x kilometres.

The distance from:

♦ Merriwell to Ryton is 5 km more than from Buxwell to Ryton

♦ Ryton to Camberly is one third of the distance from Merriwell to Ryton

♦ Umborne to Carton is 3 km more than from Buxwell to Ryton

♦ Carton to Ishlip is half the distance from Umborne to Carton

If it is the same distance from Ryton to Camberly as from Carton to Ishlip,
find the distance in kilometres from Buxwell to Ryton.

A teacher has **5 full packets** of mints and **6 single** mints.

The number of mints inside each packet is the same.

The teacher tells the class: '**Write an expression** to show **how many mints** there are **altogether**. Call the number of mints inside each packet y'.

Here are some of the expressions that the pupils write:

a   Write down **two** expressions that are correct.   *2 marks*

b   A pupil says: '*I think the teacher has a total of **56 mints**'.
      Could the pupil be correct? Write Yes or No.
      Explain how you know.   *1 mark*

Class 9H were playing a number game.

Elin said: '*Multiplying my number by 4 and then subtracting 5 gives the same answer as multiplying my number by 2 and then adding 1.*'

a   Lena called Elin's number x and formed an equation:

$$4x - 5 = 2x + 1$$

    Solve this equation and write down the **value** of x.
    Show your working.   *2 marks*

Aled said: '*Multiplying my number by 2 and then adding 5 gives the same answer as subtracting my number from 23.*'

b   **i**   Call Aled's number y and form an equation.   *1 mark*

      ii   Work out the **value** of Aled's number.   *1 mark*

1 Copy the grid and draw rectangle R.

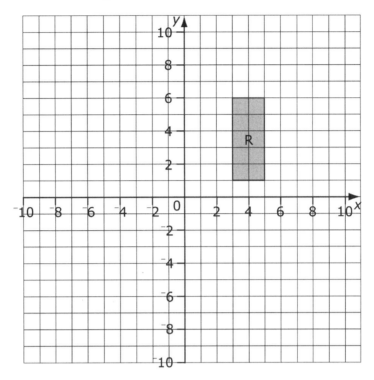

a Reflect R in the line $x = 2$. Label the new shape R'.

b Reflect R in the line $y = {}^-1$. Label the new shape R''.

c Reflect R in the line $x = {}^-2$. Label the new shape R'''.

2 Draw axes from $^-10$ to $^+10$. On your axes, draw the shape A with coordinate vertices (1, 1), (1, 7), (6, 7), (6, 4).

a Reflect A in the line $x = 2$. Label the new shape A'.

b Reflect A in the line $y = 1$. Label the new shape A''.

c Reflect A in the line $x = 0$. Label the new shape A'''.

3 Draw axes from $^-10$ to $^+10$. On your axes, draw the shape B with coordinate vertices (2, 2), (2, 6), (5, 6), (5, 3), (4, 3), (4, 2).

a Reflect B in the line $x = 2$. Label the new shape B'.

b Reflect B in the line $y = {}^-1$. Label the new shape B''.

c What reflection sends B' to B?

d What reflection sends B'' to B?

1 Copy the grid and enlarge the shape by a scale factor of 3.

Use X as the centre of enlargement.

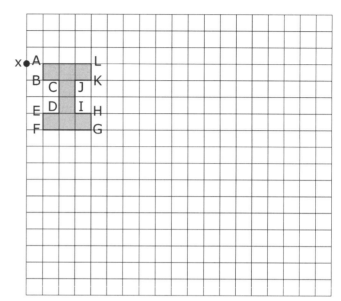

2 Copy the grid and enlarge the shape by a scale factor of 4 using X as the centre of enlargement.

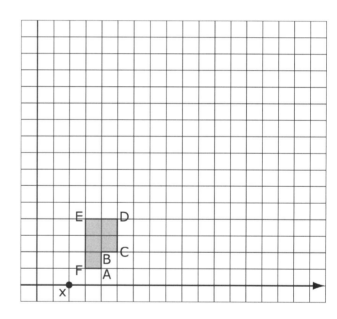

3 Draw a pair of axes from 0 to 10. Plot the points A (1, 3), B (1, 6), C (5, 3).

Draw the enlargement of triangle ABC using a scale factor of 2 and centre of enlargement (0, 3).

4 Draw a pair of axes from ⁻2 to 20. Plot the points P (2, 1), Q (1, 4), R (4, 1).

Draw the enlargement of triangle PQR using a scale factor of 4 and centre of enlargement (2, 0).

1   Here is a grid with shapes on it:

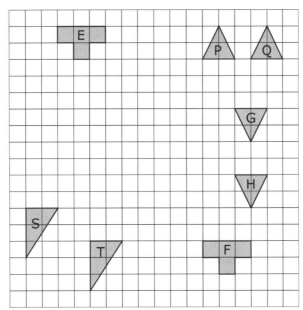

On the grid, which vectors send:

a   P to Q

b   S to T

c   G to H

d   E to F?

2   Draw axes from ⁻10 to ⁺10. On your axes, draw the shape A with coordinate vertices (2, 1), (2, 3), (5, 3), (6, 1).

a   Translate A five squares to the left and three squares down. Label the new shape A′.

b   Translate A four squares to the right and two squares up. Label the new shape A″.

c   Translate A three squares to the right and 0 squares up. Label the new shape A‴.

3   Draw axes from ⁻7 to ⁺7. On your axes, draw the shape B with coordinate vertices (0, 3), (0, 4), (5, 4), (2, 2).

a   Translate B using the vector $\begin{pmatrix} ^-1 \\ 0 \end{pmatrix}$ and label the new shape B′.

b   Translate B using the vector $\begin{pmatrix} ^-2 \\ ^+3 \end{pmatrix}$ and label the new shape B″.

c   Translate B using the vector $\begin{pmatrix} 0 \\ ^-4 \end{pmatrix}$ and label the new shape B‴.

1   Copy the grid. Draw the rectangle and label it R.

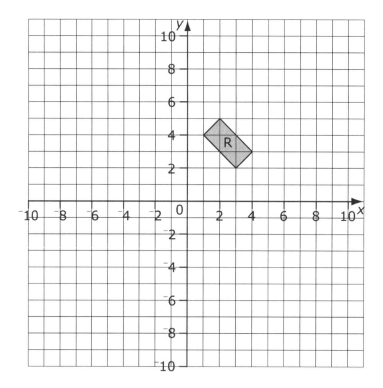

a   Rotate R through 90° clockwise about the origin and label the image R'.

b   Rotate R through 180° about the origin and label the image R''.

c   Rotate R through 270° clockwise about the origin and label the image R'''.

d   What rotation will send R''' to R?

e   What rotation will send R'' to R?

2   Draw axes from ⁻10 to 10. On your axes, draw the shape A with coordinate vertices (1, 2), (1, 7), (5, 7), (5, 2).

a   Rotate A through 90° clockwise about the origin and label the image A'.

b   Rotate A through 180° about the origin and label the image A''.

c   Rotate A through 270° clockwise about the origin and label the image A'''.

d   What rotation will send A''' to A?

e   What rotation will send A'' to A?

You will need squared paper or squared dotty paper for this homework.

Here is a 3 × 3 grid of dots:

● ● ●

● ● ●

● ● ●

Here are two different polygons drawn on a 3 × 3 grid, with a description of their symmetry properties.

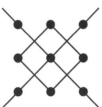

5 sides (trapezium)

no rotational symmetry

1 line of symmetry

4 sides (square)

rotational symmetry order 4

4 lines of symmetry

Activity

Draw six different polygons using 3 × 3 grids.

For each polygon that you draw:

➡ name it and state the number of sides
➡ state whether it is regular or not
➡ describe its rotational symmetry
➡ describe its reflection symmetry

1 a   Draw a grid on squared paper with *x*-axis from 0 to 10 and with *y*-axis from ⁻5 to 5.

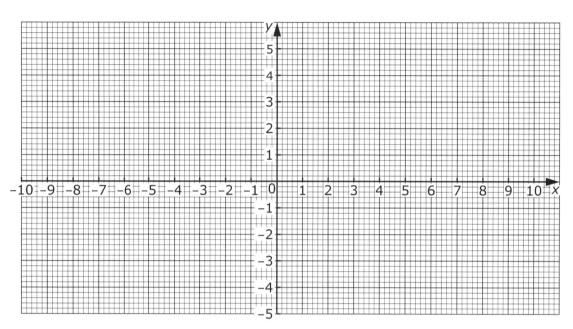

b   Draw triangle P with vertices (1, 1), (2, 1) and (2, 3).

c   Draw the line with equation *x* = 3.

d   Reflect P in the line *x* = 3 and label the image Q.

e   Draw the line with equation *x* = 6.

f   Reflect Q in the line *x* = 6 and label the image R.

g   What single transformation sends triangle P to triangle R?

h   Reflect Q in the *x*-axis and label the image S.

i   What single transformation sends triangle P to triangle S?

2   Here are two statements:

> A: Repeated reflection in two parallel lines is equivalent to a translation.

> B: Repeated reflection in two perpendicular lines is equivalent to a rotation.

Justify these statements by referring to your answers to question 1.

This shape is called an
L-triomino.
It is made from three squares.

This shape is made from two
L-triominoes. They do not overlap.
It has only **one line** of symmetry.

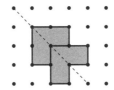

You may use a mirror or tracing paper to help you in this question.

a   On a square grid draw a **different** shape made from two
L-triominoes which do not overlap.
It must have only **one line** of symmetry.   *1 mark*

b   On your grid draw a shape made from two L-triominoes which do
not overlap.
It must have **two lines** of symmetry.   *1 mark*

This shape is made from two L-triominoes which do not overlap. It
has **rotational** symmetry of order **two**.

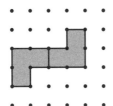

c   On a square grid draw a **different** shape made from two
L-triominoes which do not overlap.
It must have **rotational** symmetry of order **two**.   *1 mark*

d   On a square grid draw a shape made from two L-triominoes
which do not overlap.
It must have **two** lines of symmetry **and rotational** symmetry
of order **two**.   *1 mark*

S4 | Transformations

Julie has written a computer program to transform pictures of tiles.

There are **only two instructions** in her program,

Reflect vertical
or
Rotate 90° clockwise.

Reflect vertical

Rotate 90° clockwise

a Julie wants to transform the first pattern to the second pattern.

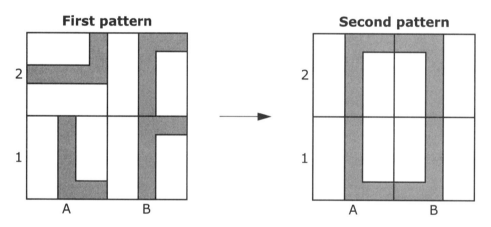

First pattern

Second pattern

Copy and complete the instructions to transform the tiles B1 and B2.
You must use only **Reflect vertical** or **Rotate 90° clockwise.**

A1 *Tile is in the correct position.*

A2 *Reflect vertical, and then Rotate 90° clockwise.*

B1 *Rotate 90° clockwise, and then* _____

B2 _____   *2 marks*

b Paul starts with the first pattern that was on the screen.

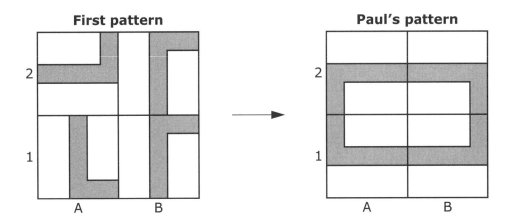

Copy and complete the instructions for the transformations of
A2, B1 and B2 to make Paul's pattern.
You must use only **Reflect vertical** or **Rotate 90° clockwise**.

A1 *Reflect vertical, and then Rotate 90° clockwise.*

A2 *Rotate 90° clockwise, and then _____*

B1 _____

B2 _____   *3 marks*

The table shows data on twelve satellites in the solar system.

It gives the orbiting distance of each satellite in kilometres.

For four satellites it also shows how long it takes them to spin around their axes measured in days (rotational period).

Name	Orbits	Distance (km)	Rotational period (days)
Adrastea	Jupiter	128 971	
Amalthea	Jupiter	181 300	0.498179
Ananke	Jupiter	21 200 000	
Ariel	Uranus	191 240	2.520379
Atlas	Saturn	137 640	
Belinda	Uranus	75 260	
Bianca	Uranus	59 160	
Callisto	Jupiter	1 883 000	16.68902
Calypso	Saturn	294 660	
Carme	Jupiter	22 600 000	
Charon	Pluto	19 640	6.38725
Cordelia	Uranus	49 750	

1 **a** Which satellite is at the greatest distance from its planet?

   b Which satellite is at the least distance?

   c Calculate the difference between the greatest and least distances to the nearest thousand.

2 **a** Round each of the distances in the table to the nearest thousand.

   b Which distances stay the same when they are rounded to the nearest thousand?
       What do you notice about these particular distances?

3 **a** Round each of the four rotational periods (last column) to the nearest:

       i 3 dp   **ii** 2 dp   **iii** 1 dp   **iv** integer

   b Find the mean rotational period and give your answer to 1 decimal place.

156 is a special number because...

◆   the sum of its digits is 12: 1 + 5 + 6 = 12

◆   12 is a factor of 156: 156 ÷ 12 = 13

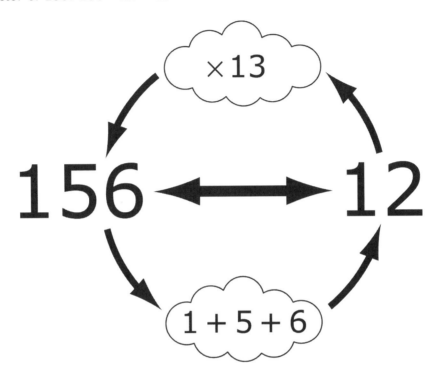

Challenge

How many other 3-digit numbers can you find that:

◆   have a sum of digits which is 12

◆   have 12 as a factor?

Extension

Investigate with numbers other than 12.

1   Use a divisibility test to decide which of these numbers are divisible by 33.
    Show your working.

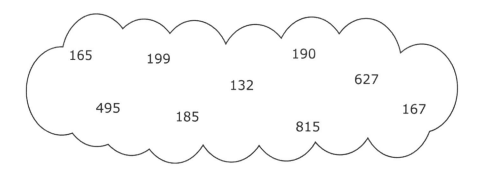

2   Write down all the factors of these numbers which are less than 30:

    a   2520

    b   18240

    c   984960

    d   44273

    What do you notice about part **d**?

The cost of admission to a swimming pool is as follows:

Adults	£3.25
Children	£1.90
Students/OAPs	£2.25

1   On a particular day, 58 adults, 43 children, 21 students and 12 OAPs used the swimming pool. How much money was collected in total?

2   In an attempt to boost attendance figures, the manager of the swimming pool reduces all admission fees by 15%.

What are the new admission fees?

3   The swimming pool is rectangular, measuring 35.8 m by 18.2 m.

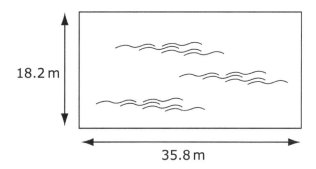

18.2 m

35.8 m

a   Calculate the perimeter of the pool in metres.

b   Calculate the area in square metres.

1 Use a 'standard method' to work the following divisions, giving answers to 1 dp.

    a $32.3 \div 5$

    b $6.10 \div 6$

    c $6.40 \div 7$

    d $85.4 \div 5$

    e $43.7 \div 8$

    f $72.6 \div 8$

    g $3.57 \div 9$

    h $12.3 \div 4$

    i $9.58 \div 3$

    j $62.6 \div 6$

2 Use a 'standard method' to work the following divisions, giving all answers to 2 dp.

    a $92.3 \div 3.2$

    b $5.10 \div 4.5$

    c $83.0 \div 51$

    d $8.54 \div 62$

    e $33.7 \div 8.2$

    f $82.4 \div 8.3$

    g $0.0547 \div 0.75$

    h $5.33 \div 32$

    i $0.258 \div 23$

    j $3.76 \div 6.2$

3 The following answers were achieved by dividing a 'mystery' whole number by 7 on a calculator. Note the answers are rounded to 3 decimal places where appropriate.

    a   2.857

    b   4.714

    c   5.857

    d   1.714

For each answer **a** to **d**, use your calculator to work out the mystery number.

Here are four improper fractions:

$\frac{37}{5}$	$\frac{49}{9}$	$\frac{58}{8}$	$\frac{14}{4}$

1 Write each of these fractions as a decimal.

2 Order the fractions from largest to smallest.

3 Write each of the fractions as a mixed number in its simplest form.

4 What answer do you get if you subtract the smallest fraction from the largest?

5 Add the four fractions together and write your answer in its simplest form.

6 Put these fractions in order, from smallest to largest.
What word is revealed?

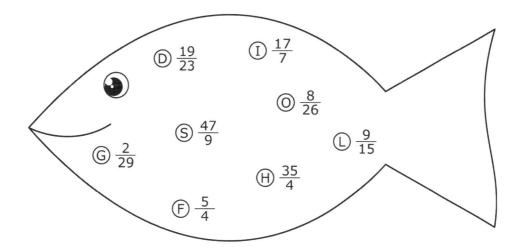

1 The cloud contains fractions, decimals and percentages.

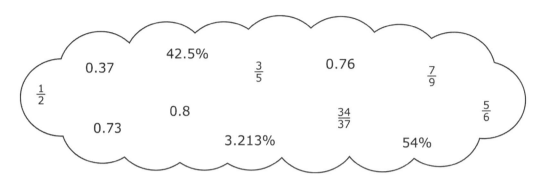

Write each of the fractions and percentages as a decimal.

Find the three numbers with the highest value and find their sum.

Show any working out you needed to do.

2 Match the fractions and percentages with the equivalent decimals in the grids. Substitute the letters to reveal the animals. The decimals are rounded to 2 dp.

E $\dfrac{3}{16}$

P 49.7%

A $\dfrac{7}{3}$

T 11%

I 89.6%

R $\dfrac{85}{12}$

Z $\dfrac{262}{63}$

L $\dfrac{16}{13}$

B $\dfrac{23}{11}$

H 81%

N 0.95%

G $\dfrac{6}{7}$

F $\dfrac{9}{13}$

0.19	1.23	0.19	0.5	0.81	2.33	0.01	0.11

0.86	0.90	7.08	2.33	0.69	0.69	0.19

4.16	0.19	2.09	7.08	2.33

1   Calculate:

    a   10% of £800

    b   5% of £800

    c   2.5% of £800

2   Calculate and show all your working:

    a   17.5% of £800

    b   35% of £800

3   Bill bought a DVD player for £93.25. VAT was then added at 17.5%.

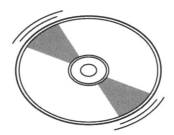

    a   How much VAT did he pay?

    b   What was the actual price he paid?

    c   Bill's friend Jenny gave him $\frac{3}{8}$ of the total price of the DVD player.

        What was the final cost to Bill?

─────────────────────────────────────── Level 5

This is how Caryl works out **15%** of **120** in her head.

10% of 120 is **12**

5% of 120 is **6**

so **15%** of 120 is **18**

a Copy and complete the following to show how Caryl can work out **17 $\frac{1}{2}$% of 240** in her head.

_____% of 240 is _____

_____% of 240 is _____

_____% of 240 is _____

so **17 $\frac{1}{2}$%** of 240 is _____   *2 marks*

b Work out **35%** of **520**.
Show your working.   *2 marks*

─────────────────────────────────────── Level 6

A drink from a machine costs **55p**.

The table shows the coins that were put into the machine one day.

Coins	Number of coins
50p	31
20p	22
10p	41
5p	59

How many cans of drink were sold that day?
Show your working   *3 marks*

Blackwater Theme Park want you to find out more about their 'typical visitor'.

They are interested in the ages of typical visitors to the park, and if large groups of visitors spend, on average, more or less than small groups of visitors.

Blackwater Park

The park covers an area of 300 square acres and has an annual turnover of 3 million pounds. Over 300 000 people a year are welcomed through the gates, with many on school trips and holiday visits.

◆ Decide what data you need to collect.

◆ Design a data collection sheet to collect this data.

Think carefully about what information you need to answer the questions.

Remember where you will be collecting the data and think about who you will be asking for information.

Remember:
On a time series graph, time is
always given in the horizontal axis.

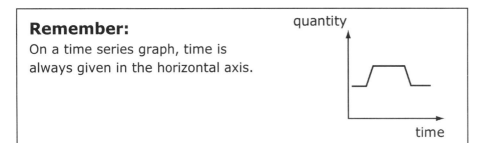

1 This table gives Jon's height in cm (to the nearest cm) on his birthday every year.

Year	1980	1981	1982	1983	1984	1985	1986	1987	1988
Jon's age	2	3	4	5	6	7	8	9	10
Height in cm	90	99	106	112	118	125	130	135	139
Year	1989	1990	1991	1992	1993	1994	1995	1996	1997
Jon's age	11	12	13	14	15	16	17	18	19
Height in cm	142	145	150	153	165	172	175	181	183

a Draw a time series graph to represent this data.
Choose what data to put on the horizontal axis.

b Comment on the trend shown by the graph.

c Which year did Jon grow most?

d Identify three key features of the graph and explain what they mean.

2 This table gives information on where confectionery is bought in a given year.

Shop	Confectionery bought
Supermarket	38%
Sweet shop	17%
Petrol station	9%
Local grocer	12%
Newsagent	20%
Other	4%

a Draw a pie chart to show this data.

b Where is most confectionery sold?

c What might be included as 'other' shops?

Debbie, Lewis and Martha independently conducted traffic surveys at different places one Monday morning between 10 am and 10.30 am. They each drew a diagram to represent the data they collected.

1   Why might it be difficult to compare the data that Debbie, Lewis and Martha have collected?

2   Redraw one or more of the diagrams so that it may be easier to compare the data.

   (You may need to put the data into a frequency table first.)

3   Compare the data that Debbie, Lewis and Martha have collected.

   Use your comparisons to suggest on which type of road they were conducting their surveys.

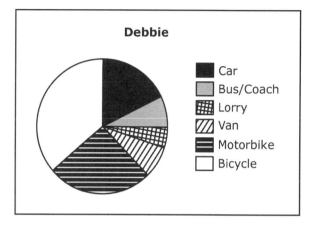

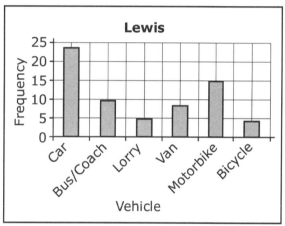

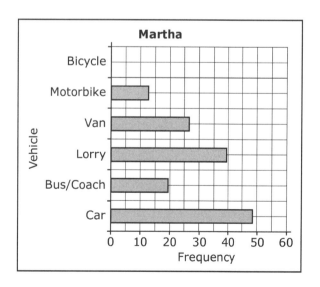

1   Molly counted the number of matches in each of 16 boxes of matches.

Her results were:

42	43	44	45	42	41	43	42
45	24	46	42	42	43	45	44

a   Calculate the range, mean, median and mode of these data.

Nina looks at the data. She believes that one of the numbers has been incorrectly recorded.

b   Which number do you think has been recorded incorrectly?
Give a reason for your answer.

c   Ignoring this number, calculate the range, mean, median and mode of the remaining 15 values.

d   Comment on the differences and similarities between your answers to parts **a** and **c**. Which data set is more reliable?

2   One-litre bottles of lemonade were emptied and their contents measured to the nearest ml. The results were:

997	995	1003	991	987	993	992	989	1002	1004

a   Use an assumed mean of 1000 ml to calculate the mean average content of the bottles.

b   The manufacturers say that the bottles contain approximately one litre.
Are they correct?

c   Calculate the range of the amounts.

d   What is this range as a percentage of one litre?

How accurate are the filling machines which fill the bottles in the factory?

Count the number of letters in each of the first fifty words on each of the pages below.

◆ Design a data collection sheet to record your results.

◆ Calculate statistics (range and an appropriate average) for your data.

> Within a short time of leaving the town, the sun began to set. As we climbed higher through the pass, the mountains were bathed in a deep red light, and the sky darkened above them, filling the whole world about me in shadow. Then I slept, and woke to darkness and black night. The carriage had stopped. We had reached the top of the Borgo Pass. I got out, found the road easily enough, and began my ascent to Castle Dracula. The landlady of the hotel had been right. It was hard going, especially at night. And cold, too. Bitterly cold. It was a cloudless night and the moon was full. In the distance I heard wolves howling. Once, I thought I saw a light flickering among the rocks above me. A pale-blue, unearthly light. I left the path and climbed towards it, but it disappeared, and as I turned to make my way back to the road, there was a movement in the shadows, and a figure stood before me.

From *Dracula*, Bram Stoker (adapted).

Minerals

Most of the known inorganic elements or minerals can be found in the human body. Only 15 are known to be essential, and must be supplied by food; these include iron, calcium, phosphorus, magnesium, sodium, chlorine, potassium, and zinc. Some are needed in very small amounts. They are called 'trace elements', and include iodine, copper, fluoride, and selenium.

Iron

Iron is needed to make haemoglobin, the substance in red blood cells which carries oxygen to parts of the body where it is needed. The oxygen is necessary for cells to work efficiently. Without enough oxygen, muscle cells do not work well and so we feel tired and lacking in energy. Brain cells do not work efficiently so we may be unable to concentrate and work well. Resistance to infection may be reduced. Shortage of iron is being seen increasingly in young children. Continued iron deficiency over a long time results in *anaemia*.

From *All about food*, Helen McGrath.

◆ Draw appropriate diagrams to compare your data.

◆ Use your graphs and statistics to comment on the similarities and differences that you have found.

a The graph shows the average heights of young children.

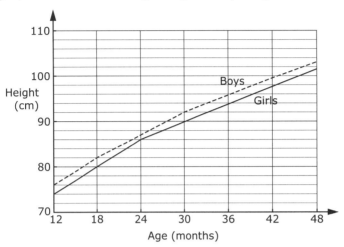

The table shows approximately how much an average **girl** grows each year between the ages of 12 and 48 months.

Copy the table and use the graph to complete it.

Age (months)	Approximate height at start (cm)	Approximate height at end (cm)	Approximate growth (cm)
12 to 24	74	86	12
24 to 36	86		
36 to 48			

2 marks

b This formula tells you how tall a **boy** is likely to be when he grows up.

Add the mother's and father's heights.
Divide by 2
Add 7cm to the result.

The boy is likely to be this height, **plus or minus 10 cm**.

Marc's mother is **168cm** tall.
His father is **194cm** tall.

What is the **greatest** height Marc is likely to be when he grows up?

Show your working. *2 marks*

school has 5 Year groups.

0 pupils from the school took part in a sponsored swim.

ara drew this graph.

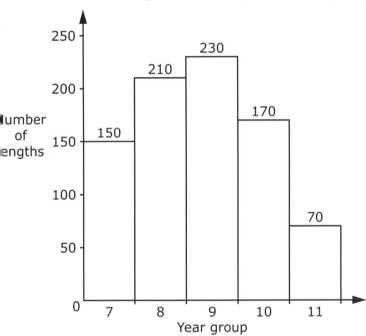

Number of lengths swum by each Year group

Look at the graph.

Did **Year 10** have **fewer** pupils taking part in the swim than **Year 7**?

Write down the correct box.

☐ Yes   ☐ No   ☐ Cannot tell

Explain your answer.   *1 mark*

Use the graph to work out the mean number of lengths swum by each of the 80 pupils.

Show your working.   *2 marks*

1   A colour spinner has five equal sectors with the colours grey, red, orange, purple and black. It is spun twice.

Draw a sample space diagram to show all the possible outcomes.

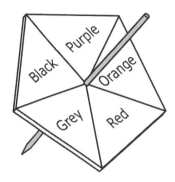

Find the probability that:

a   The spinner lands on grey or red.

b   The spinner lands on orange on both spins.

c   The spinner lands on the same colour on both spins.

2   Phil has three coins in her pocket, 2p, 10p and 20p.

She has four coins in her purse, 1p, 10p, 20p and 50p.

She chooses two coins, one from her pocket and one from her purse.

Draw a sample space diagram to show all the possible outcomes.

Find the probability that:

a   She chooses a total of 3p.

b   She chooses a total of 30p.

c   She chooses silver coins.

3   Two fair dice are thrown.

The difference between the scores is calculated.

Draw a sample space diagram to show all the possible outcomes.

Find the probability that the difference is:

a   5   **b**   0

c   an even number   **d**   a prime number

A tube of sweets has a single-digit number printed on the inside of its lid.

These are the possible lids:

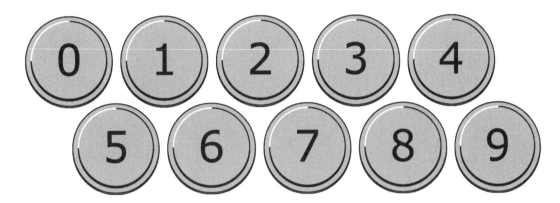

Describe how you could estimate how many tubes of sweets to buy to make sure you get each of the digits of the year you were born.

Use a simulation method to estimate how many tubes of sweets you might need to buy.

Repeat the simulation 10 times in total.

Comment on your answers.

Probability maze

Here is a probability maze, which is run by Algernon the mouse.

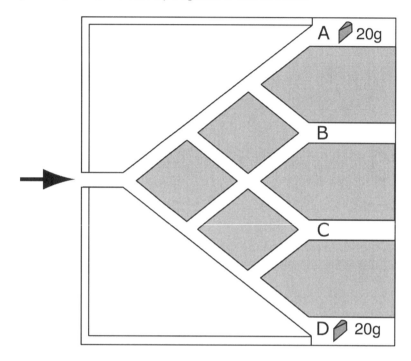

To run the probability maze Algernon:

◆   Enters at the left-hand side.

◆   At each junction he has an equal chance of going to the left or to the right.

◆   There is 20g of cheese for him at A or D.

◆   There is nothing at B or C.

Calculate the probability that he runs to:

a   A

b   B

c   C

d   D

If Algernon ran the maze 100 times, but ate 2g of cheese after every time, would he have any cheese left over at the end?

A coin has two sides, heads and tails.

heads   tails

a   Chris is going to toss a coin.

What is the **probability** that Chris will get **heads**?

Write your answer as a **fraction**.   *1 mark*

b   Sion is going to toss **2** coins.

Copy and complete the table to show the different results he could get.

First coin	Second coin
heads	heads

1 mark

c   Sion is going to toss **2** coins.

What is the **probability** that he will get **tails** with **both** his coins?

Write your answer as a **fraction**.   *1 mark*

d   Dianne tossed one coin.

She got tails.

Dianne is going to toss another coin.

What is the **probability** that she will get **tails again** with her next coin?

Write your answer as a **fraction**.   *1 mark*

D4 Probability experiments

This dice with 4 faces has one blue,
one green, one red and one yellow face.

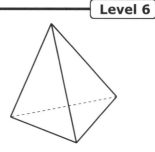

Five pupils did an experiment to investigate
whether the dice was biased or not.

The data they collected are shown in this table.

Pupil's name	Number of throws	Face landed on			
		Red	Blue	Green	Yellow
Peter	20	9	7	2	2
Caryl	60	23	20	8	9
Shana	250	85	90	36	39
Keith	40	15	15	6	4
Paul	150	47	54	23	26

a   Which pupil's data is **most likely** to give the best estimate of
the probability of getting each colour on the dice?

Explain your answer. *1 mark*

The pupils collected all the data together.

Number of throws	Face landed on			
	Red	Blue	Green	Yellow
520	179	186	75	80

b   Consider the data.

Write down whether you think the dice is biased or unbiased,
and explain your answer. *1 mark*

c   From the data work out the probability of the dice landing
on the blue face. *1 mark*

d   From the data work out the probability of the dice landing
on the green face. *1 mark*

1 Solve these equations:

   a $4x - 20 = 2x + 16$

   b $50 - 3x = 2x - 25$

   c $8 - 3x = 2x - 17$

   d $40 - x = x - 22$

   e $11 - 3x = 21 - 8x$

   f $3x + 5 = 180 - 2x$

   g $3x + 11 = 5x - 35$

   h $3(x + 7) = 9(x - 5)$

   i $5(x + 2) = {}^-6(1 - x)$

   j $2(3x - 7) = 2(x + 5)$

2 Solve these equations involving algebraic fractions:

   a $\dfrac{x}{2} + 7 = 19$

   b $\dfrac{x}{8} - 16 = 24$

   c $\dfrac{50}{x} = 10$

   d $30 - \dfrac{x}{2} = 16$

   e $\dfrac{x + 2}{3} = \dfrac{x - 1}{2}$

   f $\dfrac{5}{x + 1} = \dfrac{{}^-7}{2}$

In questions 1 to 3, you are given a formula with arrows leading from it.
Each set of arrows leads to a different subject of the formula.

◆ Copy and complete each diagram.
◆ Use the rectangular boxes to show your working.
◆ Write your answers in the oval shapes.
◆ The first one has been partially completed for you.

1

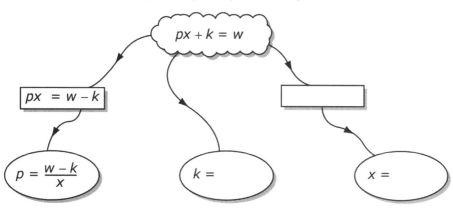

$px + k = w$

$px = w - k$

$p = \dfrac{w - k}{x}$

$k =$

$x =$

2

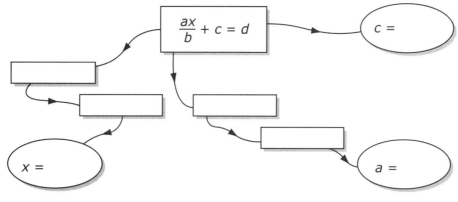

$\dfrac{ax}{b} + c = d$

$c =$

$x =$

$a =$

3

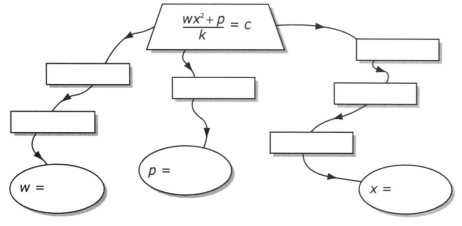

$\dfrac{wx^2 + p}{k} = c$

$w =$

$p =$

$x =$

Copy this grid.

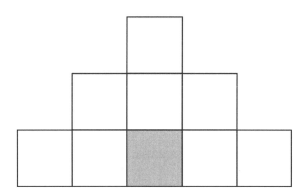

Solve these equations.

Insert the solutions into the grid so that they fit the squares.

Only place a single digit in any square.

1 $5x - 120 = 3x + 394$

2 $2(x + 5) = 6(x - 15)$

3 $3(y - 12) - 2(y - 9) = 18$

4 $80 - 2x = 2x - 24$

5 $4(z - 8) - 2(z - 9) = 7(z - 57)$

6 $2(90 - p) - (p - 50) = (p + 30) - (p + 10)$

1   Match each sequence given in Box A with its general term formula in Box B.

Box A	
a	9, 13, 17, 21, ...
b	10, 40, 90, 160, ...
c	7, 10, 15, 22, ...
d	14, 13, 12, 11, ...

Box B	
A	$T(n) = n^2 + 6$
B	$T(n) = 15 - n$
C	$T(n) = 10n^2$
D	$T(n) = 4n + 5$

2   Derive the first five terms of these sequences.

a $T(n) = 5n + 1$

b $T(n) = 7n - 4$

c $T(n) = n^2 - 1$

d $T(n) = 2n^2$

e $T(n) = \dfrac{1}{3n}$

f $T(n) = \dfrac{n+1}{n+2}$

3   For each sequence:

   ◆   decide whether it is linear or quadratic

   ◆   find a formula for $T(n)$, the general term

a   12, 23, 34, 45, 56, ...

b   1, 7, 13, 19, 25, ...

c   8, 6, 4, 2, 0, ...

d   11, 14, 19, 26, 35, ...

1 For each diagram, copy and complete the table. Use the table to find a formula for *T* (total number of tiles) in terms of *n* (pattern number) and explain why it works.

n Pattern no.	*T* Total tiles
1	
2	
3	
4	

 Formula Why it works

a

 , , 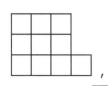 , 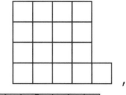 , ...

b

 , 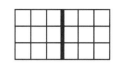 ,  , ...

2 When friends meet, one friend will kiss the other's cheek, and the other friend will then return this kiss.

a Copy and complete this table for the number of kisses:

No. of friends *F*	1	2	3	4	5
No. of kisses *K*	0	2			

b Using the method of differences, find a formula relating *F* to *K*.

c Explain why the formula works.

3 The formula for each diagram is given where *T* = total number of tiles and *n* = pattern number. Explain why the formula works.

a $T(n) = (n + 2)^2 - n^2$

 , , 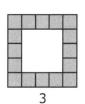 , ...

1   2   3

b $T(n) = n^2 + 2n$

 , , ...

1   2   3

127

Task 1: T-shapes

Take a 100 square (10 × 10 grid):

Draw a T-shape in the grid in a position of your choice (see example).

◆ Investigate the total of the T-shape.

For example,

$T(53) = 182$

42	43	44
	53	

What would the total be for $T(n)$?

◆ Does the result change in different sized grids?

For example, 9 × 9, 8 × 8, $m \times m$?

◆ Does the result change for different shapes?

1	2	3	4	5	6	7	8	9	10
11	12	13	14	15	16	17	18	19	20
21	22	23	24	25	26	27	28	29	30
31	32	33	34	35	36	37	38	39	40
41	42	43	44	45	46	47	48	49	50
51	52	53	54	55	56	57	58	59	60
61	62	63	64	65	66	67	68	69	70
71	72	73	74	75	76	77	78	79	80
81	82	83	84	85	86	87	88	89	90
91	92	93	94	95	96	97	98	99	100

Task 2: The jigsaw puzzle

Square jigsaws are made up of corner pieces (C), edge pieces (E) and middle pieces (M).

Investigate how many of each type there are in an $n \times n$ jigsaw.

What if the jigsaw was rectangular ($m \times n$)?

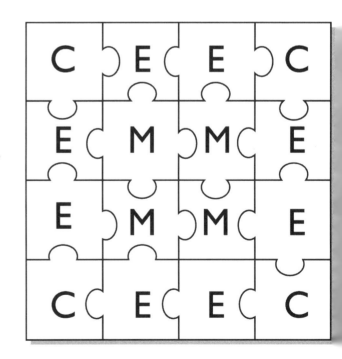

1 The graph $y = x + 1$ has been drawn on this grid.

  a Copy the graph and add three graphs of your own, parallel to $y = x + 1$.

  b For each graph that you have drawn, write down four coordinates and use these to establish the equation of the graph.

  c What do you notice? Are any of the numbers in your equations important? Why?

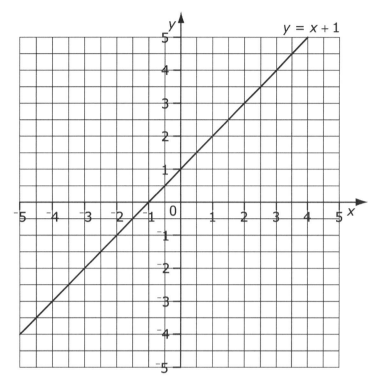

2 The graph $y = x$ has been drawn on this grid.

  a Copy the graph and add three graphs of your own, steeper than $y = x$ but still passing through the origin $(0, 0)$.

  b For each graph, establish its equation.

  c What do you notice?

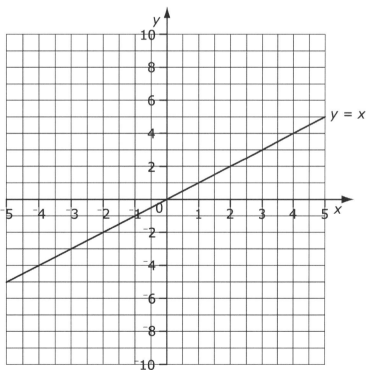

1 For each container, sketch a graph of the depth of water against time, when water drips steadily into the container.

a   **b**   **c**   **d**

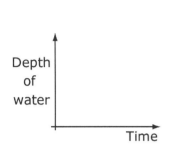

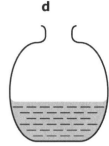

2 Match the distance–time graphs with the stated journeys.

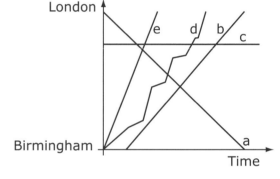

- A: An express train travelling from Birmingham to London.
- B: A steam train travelling from Birmingham to London.
- C: A signalman sitting in his box at Watford.
- D: A cargo train travelling from London to Birmingham.
- E: A passenger train travelling from Birmingham to London.

3 Construct a sketch graph to show:

a Daylight hours against time of year.

b Size of telephone bill against hours talking to a friend on the phone.

c A car coming to a stop at a set of traffic lights, after travelling at constant speed along a road.

d The weight of a newspaper boy's bag as he travels on his round.

4 Explain what is happening in the following graphs:

a   **b**   **c**

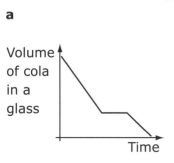
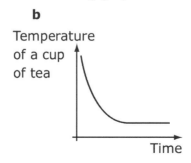
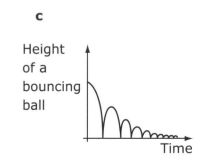

Level 5

Steve is making a series of patterns with black and grey square tiles.

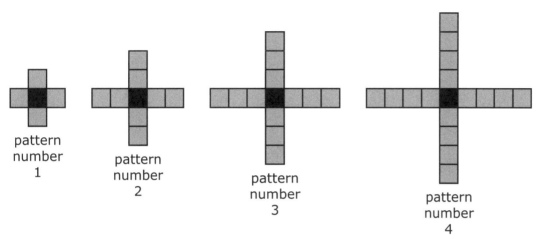

pattern number 1

pattern number 2

pattern number 3

pattern number 4

a Each pattern has **1 black tile** at the **centre.**

Each **new** pattern has **more grey tiles** than the one before.

How many **more** grey tiles does Steve add each time he make a new pattern? *1 mark*

b Steve says: *'The rule for finding the number of tiles in pattern number N is **number of tiles = 4 × N + 1**.'*

The **1** in Steve's rule represents the **black tile.**

What does the **4 x N** represent? *1 mark*

c Steve wants to make **pattern number 15.**

How many **black** tiles and how many **grey** tiles does he need? *1 mark*

d Steve uses **41 tiles** altogether to make a pattern.

What is the number of the pattern he makes? *1 mark*

e Steve has **12 black** tiles and **80 grey** tiles.

What is the number of the **biggest** pattern Steve can make? *1 mark*

Selma is investigating the number of pins needed to pin squares of paper to a wall display.

First she tried 4 pins in each square, like this.

Then she tried using 3 pins.

Then she tried using 2 pins.

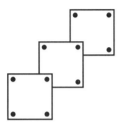
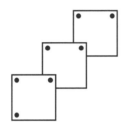
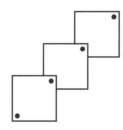

She drew graphs to show her results.

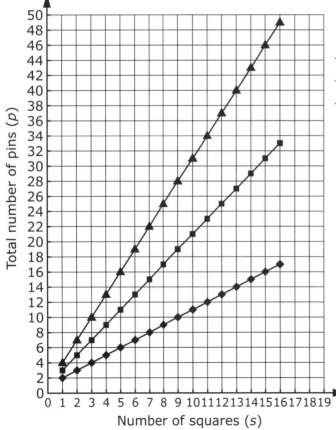

The ▲s give the graph $p = 3s + 1$

The ■s give the graph $p = 2s + 1$

The ◆s give the graph $p = s + 1$

Level 6

Selma has 16 pins.

a **i** Use the correct graph to find the number of squares she can pin up with 4 pins in each square. *1 mark*

   ii How many squares can she pin up with 3 pins in each square? *1 mark*

b The line through the points for $p = 3s + 1$ climbs more steeply than the lines through the points for $p = 2s + 1$ and $p = s + 1$.

Which part of the equation $p = 3s + 1$ tells you how steep the line is? *1 mark*

c Draw a grid like the one above and plot three points to show the graph for 8 pins in each square.

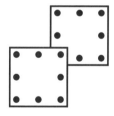

2 marks

d What is the equation of this graph? *1 mark*

You will need compasses and a protractor for this homework.

1 Construct a triangle ABC where AB = 3.5 cm, AC = 5.5 cm and CB = 6.5 cm.
Measure the size of the angles of the triangle.

2 Construct a triangle LMN where LM = 3 cm, MN = 3 cm and LN = 5 cm.
Measure the size of the angles of the triangle.

3 Construct a triangle PQR where PQ = 4.5 cm, QR = 8.5 cm and RP = 6.5 cm.
Measure the size of the angles of the triangle.

4 Construct a triangle EFG where EG = 5 cm, FG = 2 cm and FE = 4 cm.
Measure the size of the angles of the triangle.

5 Construct a triangle XYZ where XY = 3.8 cm, YZ = 4.8 cm and ZX = 5.8 cm.
Measure the size of the angles of the triangle.

1 Construct this quadrilateral.

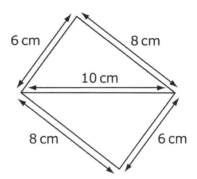

2 Construct this quadrilateral.

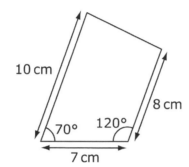

3 Construct a quadrilateral ABCD where AB = 4.3 cm, BC = 5.7 cm, CA = 6.5 cm, AD = 6.5 cm and DC = 4.8 cm.

4 Construct the quadrilateral PQRS where PQ = 5.5 cm, PS = 6.5 cm, QR = 4.5 cm, angle P = 80° and angle Q = 101°.

5 A field has dimensions as shown below.

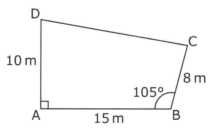

Draw a scale diagram using 1 cm to represent 1 m.

From your diagram find:

a the distance AC

b the distance DB

c the perimeter of the field

1 Construct nets of the following solids:

  a cube with sides 2 cm

  b tetrahedron with sides 4 cm

  c triangular prism

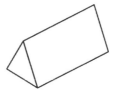

  d cuboid

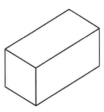

2 Describe each of these 3-D shapes in words. Which of them are prisms?

  a   **b**    **c**   **d**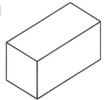

  e   **f**   **g**   **h**

Constructing perpendiculars

1   Carefully copy this diagram.

   You may wish to use tracing paper.

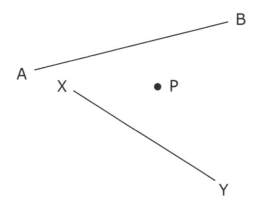

   a   Construct the perpendicular from P to the line AB.

   Label point C where the perpendicular meets AB.

   b   Construct the perpendicular from P to the line XY.

   Label point Z where the perpendicular meets XY.

   c   Measure:

   i   length AC

   ii   length XZ

   a   Using a pair of compasses, construct a triangle with sides 4.5 cm, 5.5 cm and 6 cm.

   b   Using a ruler, mark off the midpoint of each side of the triangle.

   c   Construct the perpendicular from each midpoint.

   d   All three perpendiculars should intersect at the same point inside the triangle.
   Mark this point clearly.

This is an 8–circle.

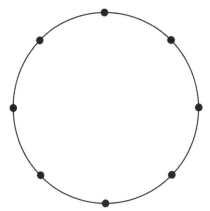

You can draw polygons on an 8-circle.

Here is an isosceles triangle.

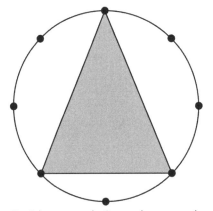

2 sides equal, 2 angles equal.

1 line of reflection symmetry.

Rotational symmetry order 1.

Activity

Trace the 8-circle at the top of the page at least six times.

Draw at least six different triangles or quadrilaterals.

For each shape that you draw, describe:

◆   its side and angle properties

◆   its symmetry properties

◆   any parallel or perpendicular sides

◆   any diagonal properties

ctagons and squares combine to form an interesting tessellation pattern.

ou can see variations of this pattern in many shopping arcades and kitchens.

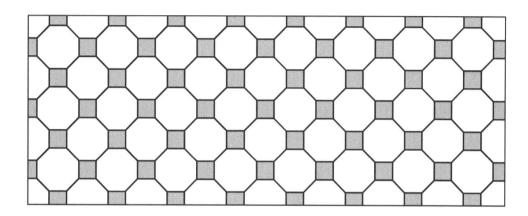

ctivity

Draw two tessellation patterns that use more than one shape.

For each pattern that you draw, explain why it tessellates by referring to its interior angles.

The sketch shows the net of a triangular prism.

The net is folded up and glued to make the prism.

a   Which edge is **tab 1** glued to?
Copy the diagram and label this edge A.

b   Which edge is **tab 2** glued to?
Label this edge B.

c   The corner marked ● meets two other corners.
Label these two other corners ●

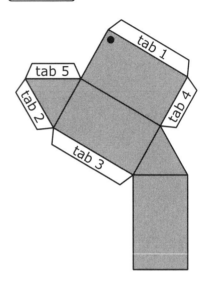

3 marks

Darren draws a net with a tab to make a cuboid.

He puts a ● in a corner of one of the faces.

Darren folds the net up.

a   Which edge will the tab be stuck to?
Copy the net and write T on the edge that
the tab will be stuck to.

b   Which two corners will meet the corner with a ● ?

On your net put a ● in each corner that
meets the corner with a ● .

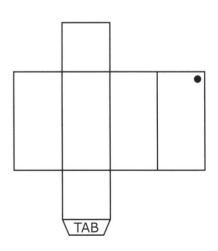

3 marks